THE SENIOR ISSUES COLLECTION

COLLECTION EDITOR:
GILLDA LEITENBERG

WORK AND LEISURE

EDITED BY TARA J. FENWICK

To my brother Jamie, my brother Rob,
and my sister Jennifer, who have each
changed the world in their own
ways through their work.

McGraw-Hill Ryerson Limited

Toronto • New York • Auckland • Bogotá
Caracas • Lisbon • London • Madrid • Mexico • Milan
New Delhi • San Juan • Singapore • Sydney • Tokyo

Work and Leisure
The Senior Issues Collection

ISBN 0-07-551694-2

1 2 3 4 5 6 7 8 9 10   BG   4 3 2 1 0 9 8 7 6 5

Printed and bound in Canada

Canadian Cataloguing in Publication Data

Main entry under title:

Work and leisure

(The Senior issues collection)
ISBN 0-07-551694-2

1. Readers (Secondary). 2. Readers – Work.
3. Readers – Leisure. 4. Work – Literary
collection. 5. Leisure – Literary collection.
I. Fenwick, Tara J. II. Series.

PE1127.W65W67 1995   808'.0427   C95-932080-6

Editor: *Kathy Evans*
Supervising Editor: *Nancy Christoffer*
Permissions Editor: *Jacqueline Donovan*
Production Co-ordinator: *Yolanda Pigden*
Proofreader: *Gail Marsden*
Designer: *Mary Opper*
Typesetter: *Pages Design Ltd.*
Photo Researcher: *Elaine Freedman*
Cover Illustrator: *Harvey Chan*

The editors wish to thank reviewer William Stratton for his comments and advice.

This book was manufactured in Canada using acid-free and recycled paper.

Contents

Introduction

What does the word "work" mean to you?

When I looked up "work" in my thesaurus, I was amazed to find long lists of words describing work as plain awful. Drudgery, toil, burdensome, agonizing, grind, labour, humdrum, routine...you get the picture. Some of the writers in this anthology describe work and their jobs in the same sorts of ways.

I was amazed to find this because to many people I've met, the activity of work is mostly satisfying. What would be the purpose of living without my work, I wonder? I write, I teach, I research, I learn and study, I travel and talk to people, and write about the stories they tell me. This isn't drudgery at all. I guess I'm just lucky to be able to do work that I love.

I wonder—what is really the difference between work and leisure? We North Americans are probably some of the few people on Earth who have the luxury to worry about leisure. The thesaurus uses delicious sorts of words to describe leisure, like: tranquillity, peace, rest, ease, slowness, refreshment. Yet some of what I consider to be the hardest work imaginable is supposed to be "leisure." Like sitting around making dreary small talk over loud music with perfect strangers. Or panting my way uphill, drenched with sweat, on a Sunday afternoon bicycle ride.

But in my leisure time I also do the laundry and clean the garage and wash out the toilet. This is not fun. This is work. Except I don't get recognition or money for doing it. (Do you?) Still, there's a curious sense of satisfaction, a peacefulness, that comes in doing jobs like this. Even some of the yucky jobs, like cleaning vertical blinds—which my neighbour tells me must be done laboriously, one at a time—give me lots of time just to slow down and daydream without guilt. So is this leisure, or work?

You've spent most of your life up till now in everyday activities that you have sometimes called "work" and sometimes "leisure." How do you label them? What do you give your time to? Which activities give you joy? Which ones give you peace? Which ones really let you express the unique person that is you? And how is it that we somehow get trapped sometimes in activity that is demeaning, draining, or plain drudgery?

These are the questions that intrigue me. When I chose the poems and stories and articles in this anthology, I looked for writers who had something to say about these questions. I also tried to pick writers who described all sorts of different experiences. You'll find pieces about domestic work and volunteer work and employed work in different workplaces and different countries. You'll see issues raised about gender, race-ethnicity, youth and seniors, empowerment, exploitation, and unfairness. You'll read about art and craft and fitness and rest and peace. Some pieces are joyful; others are very bleak.

As you read, ask yourself, who is speaking to me in this piece? Ask, how does this person think about work, or about leisure? Ask, does this piece connect with my heart and my experiences of work and leisure?

Then ask yourself again, what does work mean to me? For in answering this question, I believe you go a long way toward deciding what you want out of life. Remember, you get what you settle for.

Tara J. Fenwick

The Grasshopper and the Ants

~

BY

AESOP

s the ants were airing their provisions one winter, a hungry Grasshopper begged a charity of them. They told him that he should have wrought in summer, if he would not have wanted in winter. Well, says the Grasshopper, but I was not idle either; for I sung out the whole season. Nay then, said they, you'll even do well to make a merry year of it, and dance in winter to the tune that you sung in summer.

Action and industry is the business of a wise and a good man, and nothing is so much to be despised as slothfulness.

Work is Love

BY

ANONYMOUS

Work is love made visible.
And if you cannot work with love
But only with distaste, it is better
That you should leave your work and
Sit at the gate of the temple and take
Alms from those who work with joy.

from

The Problem of Leisure

~

BY

WITOLD

RYBCZYNSKI

sk anyone how long they spend at work and they can tell you exactly; it is more difficult to keep track of leisure. For one thing, it is irregular; for another, it varies from person to person. For some, cutting the lawn is a burden; for others it is a pleasurable pastime. Going to the mall can be a casual Saturday outing, or it can be a chore. Most would count watching television as leisure, but what about Sunday brunch? Sometimes the same activity—walking the dog—can be a pleasure, sometimes not depending on the weather. Finally, whether an activity is part of our leisure depends as much on our frame of mind as anything else.

Surveys of leisure habits often show diverging results. Two recent surveys, by the University of Maryland and by Michigan's Survey Research Center, both suggest that most Americans enjoy about thirty-nine hours of leisure time weekly. On the other hand, a 1988 survey conducted by the National Research Center of the Arts came to a very different conclusion and found that "Americans report a median 16.6 hours of leisure time each week." The truth is probably somewhere in between.

Less surprising, given the number of people working more than forty-nine hours a week, was the National Research Center's conclusion that most Americans have suffered a decline in weekly leisure time of 9.6 hours over the last fifteen years. The nineteenth-century activists who struggled so hard for a shorter workweek and more free time would have been taken aback by this statistic—what had happened to the "Eight Hours for What We Will?"

There are undoubtedly people who work longer hours out of personal ambition, to escape problems at home, or from compulsion. The term "workaholic" (a postwar Americanism) is recent, but addiction to work is not—Thomas Jefferson, for example, was a compulsive worker, as was G.K. Chesterton—and there is no evidence that there are more such people today than in the past. Of course, for many, longer hours are not voluntary—they are obliged to work more merely to make ends meet. This has been particularly true since the 1970s, when poverty in America began to increase, but since the shrinking of leisure time began during the prosperous 1960s, economic need isn't the only explanation.

Twenty years ago Staffan Linder, a Swedish sociologist, wrote a book about the paradox of increasing affluence and decreasing leisure time in the United States. Following in Lippmann's steps, Linder observed that in a prosperous consumer society there was a conflict between the market's promotion of luxury goods and the individual's leisure time. When work hours were first shortened, there were few luxury items available to the general public, and the extra free time was generally devoted to leisure. With the growth of the so-called "leisure industry," people were offered a choice: more free time or more spending? Only the wealthy could have both. If the average person wanted to indulge in expensive recreations such as skiing or sailing, or to buy expensive entertainment devices, it would be necessary to work more—to trade his or her free time for overtime or a second job. Whether because of the effectiveness of advertising or from simple acquisitiveness, most people chose spending over more free time.

Linder's thesis was that economic growth caused an increasing scarcity of time, and that statistics showing an increase in personal incomes were not necessarily a sign of growing prosperity. People were earning more because they were working more. A large percentage of free time was being converted into what he called "consumption time," and mirrored a shift from "time-intensive" to "goods-intensive" leisure. According to *U.S. News & World Report*, Americans now spend more than $13 billion annually on sports clothing; put another way, about 1.3 billion hours of potential leisure time are exchanged for leisure wear—for increasingly elaborate running shoes, certified hiking shorts, and monogrammed warm-up suits. In 1989, to pay for these indulgences, more workers than ever before—6.2 percent—held a second, part-time job....

Even if one chooses to consume less and stay at home, there are other things that cut into free time. Commuting to and from work takes longer than it used to. So does shopping—the weekly trip to the mall consumes more time than a stroll to the neighborhood corner store. Decentralized suburban life, which is to say American life, is based on the automobile. Parents become chauffeurs, ferrying their children back and forth to dance classes, hockey games, and the community pool. At home, telephone answering machines have to be played back, the household budget entered into the personal computer, the lawn mower dropped off at the repair shop, the car—or cars—serviced. All these convenient labor-saving devices relentlessly eat into our discretionary time. For many executives, administrators, and managers, the reduction of leisure time is also the result of office technology that brings work to the home. Fax machines, paging devices, and portable computers mean that taking work home at night is no longer difficult or voluntary. Even the contemplative quiet of the morning automobile commute is now disrupted by the presence of the cellular telephone.

There is no contradiction between the surveys that indicate a reversing trend, resulting in less free time, and the claim that the weekend dominates our leisure. Longer work hours and more overtime cut mainly into weekday leisure. So do longer commuting, driving the kids, and Friday-night shopping. The weekend—or what's left of it, after Saturday household chores—is when we have time to relax.

But the weekend has imposed a rigid schedule on our free time, which can result in a sense of urgency ("soon it will be Monday") that is at odds with relaxation. The weekly rush to the cottage is hardly leisurely, nor is the compression of various recreational activities into the two-day break. The freedom to do something has become the obligation to do something, just as Chesterton foretold, and the list of dutiful recreations includes strenuous disciplines intended for self-improvement (fitness exercises, jogging, bicycling), competitive sports (tennis, golf), and skill-testing pastimes (sailing, skiing).

Recreations such as tennis or sailing are hardly new, but before the arrival of the weekend, for most people, they were chiefly seasonal activities. Once a year, when vacation time came around, tennis racquets were removed from the back of the cupboard, swimwear was taken out of mothballs, skis were dusted off. The accent was less on technique than on having a good time. It was like playing Scrabble at the summer cottage: no one remembers all the rules, but everyone can still enjoy the game. Now the availability of free time every weekend has changed this casual attitude. The very frequency of weekend recreations allows continual participation and continual improvement, which encourage the development of proficiency and skill.

Skill is necessary since difficulty characterizes modern recreations. Many nineteenth-century amusements, such as rowing, were not particularly involved and required little instruction; mastering windsurfing, on the other hand, takes considerable practice and dexterity—which is part of the attraction. Even relatively simple games are complicated by the need to excel. Hence the emphasis on professionalism, which is expressed by the need to have the proper equipment and the correct costume (especially the right shoes). The desire for mastery isn't limited to outdoor recreations; it also includes complicated hobbies such as woodworking, electronics, and automobile restorations. All this suggests that the modern weekend is characterized by not only the sense of obligation to do something but the obligation to do it *well.*

The desire to do something well, whether it is sailing a boat—or building a boat—reflects a need that was previously met in the workplace. Competence was shown on the job—holidays were for messing around. Nowadays the situation is reversed. Technology has removed craft from most occupations. This is true in assembly-line jobs, where almost no training or experience, hence no skill, is required, as well as in most service positions (store clerks, fast-food attendants) where the only talent required is to learn how to smile and say, "have a good day." But it's also increasingly true in such skill-dependent work as house construction, where the majority of parts come ready-made from the factory and the carpenter merely assembles them, or automobile repair, which consists largely in replacing one throwaway part with another. Nor is the reduction of skills limited to manual work. Memory, once the prerequisite skill of the white-collar worker, has been rendered superfluous by computers; teachers, who once needed dramatic skills, now depend on mechanical aids such as slide projectors and video machines; in politics, oratory has been killed by the thirty-second sound bite.

Hence an unexpected development in the history of leisure. For many, weekend free time has become not a chance to escape work but a chance to create work that is more meaningful—to work at recreation—in order to realize the personal satisfactions that the workplace no longer offers.

"Leisure" is the most misunderstood word in our vocabulary. We often use the words "recreation" and "leisure" interchangeably—recreation room, rest and recreation, leisure suit, leisure industry—but they really embody two different ideas. Recreation carries with it a sense of necessity and purpose. However pleasurable this antidote to work may be, it's a form of active employment, engaged in with a specific end in mind—a refreshment of the spirit, or the body, or both. Implicit in this idea of renewal—usually organized renewal—is the notion that recreation is both a consequence of work and a preparation for more of it.

Leisure is different. That was what Lippmann was getting at when he contrasted commercial recreation with individual leisure. Leisure is not tied to work the way that recreation is—leisure is self-contained. The root of the word is the Latin *licere* which means "to be permitted," suggesting that leisure is about freedom. But freedom for what? According to Chesterton's cheerful view, leisure was above all an opportunity to do nothing. When he said, "doing nothing," however, he was describing not emptiness but an occasion for reflection and contemplation, a chance to look inward rather than outward. A chance to tend one's garden, as Voltaire put it. That is why Chesterton called this kind of leisure "the most precious, the most consoling, the most pure and holy."

Bertrand Russell placed leisure into a larger historical context in his essay, "In Praise of Idleness." "Leisure is essential to civilization," he wrote, "and in former times leisure for the few was only rendered possible by the labours of the many. But their labours were valuable, not because work is good, but because leisure is good." Russell, a member of the aristocracy, pointed out that it had been precisely the leisure classes, not the laborers, who had written the books, invented the philosophies, produced the sciences, and cultivated the arts. But he was not arguing for a continuation of the class system; on the contrary, he proposed extending the leisure that had previously been reserved for the few to the many. This was an explicit attack on the work ethic, which he considered a device to trick people into accepting a life without leisure. In his view, the trick hadn't succeeded; working men and women had no illusions about work—they understood it was merely a necessary means to a livelihood.

Russell's underlying argument was that we should free ourselves from the guilt about leisure that modern society has imposed on us. Hence the use of terms such as "idleness" and "doing nothing," which were intended as a provocation to a society that placed the highest value on "keeping busy." Both Russell and Chesterton agreed with Aristotle, who considered leisure the aim of life. "We work," he wrote, "to have leisure."

A
New Vision of
Livelihood

Where Does Our Work
Fit in the Cosmos?

BY

MATTHEW

FOX

L et me tell you a story. Three years ago, I was speaking in Port Huron, Michigan, and they had just that week closed down a car factory, four thousand workers thrown out of work within a week. Now speaking in a church to about seven hundred, eight hundred people and before I began, I said to myself, "Am I going to tell the whole truth or part of the truth?" and I said, "Well, I leave town tomorrow so I'll tell the whole truth." So I got up in front of these people and I said: First I want to extend my empathy to everybody here who has been affected by this layoff and of course the community has to band together and create the safety net, the retraining and the compassion for these people, and so forth. However, I want to say this: Maybe something bigger is happening here than just the closing down of a particular family's livelihood. Perhaps we have to ask the question today whether we need a lot more cars on the planet. There are already 600 million automobiles and they are a cause of a lot of our troubles, and the same is true for the defense industry. We are going through the same thing in California. You might say, "Well we've always built cars in Port Huron or we've always had military bases in

*California." We have to go deeper and say yes, but what work does
Gaia ask of our generation today? What work [is it that] future generations [are] asking of us today? And frankly, I don't think it's a lot
more cars or a lot more military bases.*

- *Let me share with you what Studs Terkel says about work. He says,
"Work is about daily meaning as well as daily bread. For recognition as well as cash; for astonishment rather than torpor; in short,
for a sort of life rather than a Monday through Friday sort of
dying.... We have a right to ask of work that it include meaning,
recognition, astonishment, and life."*

- *The* Tao Te Ching, *the Chinese scriptures, says, "In work do what
you enjoy." There's a difference between job and work. A job is
something we often do to pay our bills. Work touches your heart and
it has to touch other people's hearts. If there's one question I would
ask to awaken us to spiritual work, it would be, "How does your
work touch the joy in you and what joy does your work bring out in
others?"*

- *Lester Brown, head of Worldwatch Institute, whose job it is to go
around the world collecting all the scientific data about the earth,
said we have 20 years left to bring about the environmental revolution. The environmental revolution will be just as basic as the
Industrial Revolution. It will affect our relationships for everything—work, business, banking, farming—just as the Industrial
Revolution did 300 years ago, or the agricultural revolution did
10 000 years ago. Imagine how moving from hunting/gathering to
agriculture changed everything. It made cities possible. It made
specialists in raising food possible so others were free to do other
things. Tremendous human revolution. Now Brown says the environmental revolution will be just as all-encompassing a change, a
transformation, but the difference is that we only have 20 years to
pull it off. So every one of us, no matter what our age or what our
task and job and gifts, is part of this environmental revolution. It's
the real work that needs to be done. He said the number one obsta-
cle to bringing this environmental revolution off is human inertia.
  Inertia is a sin of the spirit. It's what our ancestors called one of
the sins of the spirit, "acedia." Saint Thomas Aquinas said acedia is*

a lack of energy to begin new things. Being a couch potato. And it's rampant in our culture and it's about lack of energy. And so what would be the opposite of acedia? Zeal. Energy. There's the cure. There's the medicine for what's holding back the environmental revolution. If inertia is the correct analysis that Lester Brown is giving us, where do we find zeal? Aquinas has an incredible statement on that. He says that zeal comes from an intense experience of the beauty of things. To overcome the inertia that is overcoming us, that is contributing so substantively to the demolition of this planet, we have to fall in love again. We think falling in love is about finding a mate once or a couple of times in one's life. It's bigger than that, folks. You can fall in love with the galaxy. There are 10 000 species of wildflowers to fall in love with. And there are trees and forests and whales and fish.

Picking Potatoes

BY

DAVID

WEALE

hey were long days, easily the longest of my life. I recall hour after desolate hour on my knees, reaching for potatoes which had been thrown this way and that by the digger, then picking up the basket and dumping it in the bag, and then the whole thing over again, and over again, and over again. It was torture, and each day seemed an eon. I remember clearly that bright October afternoon in a field in Sherbrooke when the sun stopped in the sky. I was sure of it. Every time I checked it was in exactly the same place. Finally I turned my face up and said out loud, "Get down will you. Get down, damnit."

It was hard work for a kid, especially one who hadn't been raised on a farm. I recall a skim of snow on the ground when we went out one morning, and the uncomfortable feeling of cold, damp clay packed up hard underneath all my fingernails. I also remember tripping over the tangle of dead tops as I staggered to the nearest bran bag with my heavy basket. There was the rough rub of coarse jute against raw knuckles as I attempted to dump the heavy basket, and frequent, tearful spilling and re-picking.

Everyone was assigned a stepped-off length of the drill. That was your responsibility and the only way you could get a rest during the entire day was if you managed to finish your section before the man on the tractor turned over the next. I don't think that ever happened to me, and I can recall clearly my sullen, childish anger at him for getting so far ahead. I also wondered, hatefully, why he, a strong man, should get to drive while I, a mere boy, was straining my guts trying to keep up with him. To look sideways and see three or four sections dug and waiting was enough to break your heart. I felt persecuted, and remember wishing with all my might that he would run out of gas, that a field stone would break the digger chain, that it would rain, or that the world would come to an end.

The high point of the day was dinner: roast beef (always slightly overcooked), rich dark gravy with plenty of floating onion, a mountain of mashed potatoes, turnips and carrots, homemade bread, a thick slice of pumpkin pie for dessert, and all the milk you could drink. It almost made the whole thing worthwhile. Almost.

At the end of the week I got paid. Ahh, those bills, some ones and twos, even some blue fives, and all for me! I shoved the money down deep in my pocket and exulted in the achievement it represented. I also recall flexing my biceps under my fall jacket and imagining they were much bigger and harder than those of most boys my age. There was a kind of aching satisfaction in that moment, and first faint stirrings of emergent manliness.

I Liked to Shuck Peas

BY

JOHN B.

LEE

I liked to shuck peas.
Sometimes to hear them snap
like purse hasps
or to slip my nail in the seam of the pod
and slide the thumb
so the husk hinged open to reveal
its inside self
shine like green satin
where the ripest peas free tumbled
like costume pearls
from a broken string
and the tiny
sweeter fruit clung to their stems
stuck there
like licked candy.

It was never a chore
in the sense of the slow sloshy churning of butter
nor massaging the dot of blood
through margarine for colour.

From the first plunk of the first pea
in the empty colander
to the last plush
of the last plump bead
it was
a miracle
like writing well.
I wanted to say, "Look here.
See what I've done."
And even if cousin Billy
lined them up on his knife
and spilled them into his mouth—
I remember
how they shone, lit from within.

Dirty Work

BY

ROBERT

FULGHUM

fter the dishes are washed and the sink rinsed out, there remains in the strainer at the bottom of the sink what I will call, momentarily, some "stuff." A rational, intelligent, objective person would say that this is simply a mixture of food particles too big to go down the drain, composed of bits of protein, carbohydrates, fat, and fiber. Dinner dandruff.

Furthermore, the person might add that not only was the material first sterilized by the high heat of cooking, but further sanitized by going through the detergent and hot water of the dishpan, and rinsed. No problem.

But any teenager who has been dragooned into washing dishes knows this explanation is a lie. That stuff in the bottom of the strainer is toxic waste—deadly poison—a danger to health. In other words, about as icky as icky gets.

One of the very few reasons I had any respect for my mother when I was thirteen was because she would reach into the sink with her bare hands—BARE HANDS—and pick up that lethal gunk and drop it into the garbage. To top that, I saw her reach into the wet garbage bag and fish around in there looking for a lost teaspoon BAREHANDED—a kind of mad courage. She found the spoon in a clump of coffee grounds mixed with scrambled egg remains and the end of the vegetable soup. I almost passed out when she handed it to me to rinse off. No teenager who wanted to live would have touched that without being armed with gloves, a face mask, and stainless-steel tongs.

Once, in school, I came across the French word *ordure*, and when the teacher told me it meant "unspeakable filth" I knew exactly to what it referred. We had it every night. In the bottom of the sink.

When I reported my new word to my mother at dishwashing time, she gave me her my-son-the-idiot look and explained that the dinner I had just eaten was in just about the same condition in my stomach at the moment, rotting, and it hadn't even been washed and rinsed before it went down my drain. If she had given me a choice between that news and being hit across the head with a two-by-four, I would have gone for the board.

I lobbied long and hard for a disposal and an automatic dishwasher, knowing full well that they had been invented so that *nobody* would *ever* have to touch the gunk again.

Never mind what any parent or objective adult might tell me, I knew that the stuff in the sink drainer was lethal and septic. It would give you leprosy, or something worse. If you should ever accidentally touch it, you must never touch any other part of your body with your fingers until you had scalded and soaped and rinsed your hands. Even worse, I knew that the stuff could congeal and mush up and mutate into some living thing that would crawl out of the sink during the night and get loose in the house.

Why not just use rubber gloves, you ask? Oh, come on. Rubber gloves are for sissies. Besides, my mother used her bare hands, remember. My father never came closer than three feet to the sink in his life. My mother said he was lazy. But I knew that he knew what I knew about the gunk.

Once, after dinner, I said to him that I bet Jesus never had to wash dishes and clean the gunk out of the sink. He agreed. It was the only theological discussion we ever had.

My father, however, would take a plunger to the toilet when it was stopped up with even worse stuff. I wouldn't even go in the room when he did it. I didn't want to know.

But now. Now, I am a grown-up. And have been for some time.

And I imagine making a speech to a high school graduating class. First, I would ask them, How many of you would like to be an adult, an independent, on-your-own citizen? All would raise their hands with some enthusiasm. And then I would give them this list of things that grown-ups do:

- clean the sink strainer
- plunge out the toilet
- clean up babies when they poop and pee
- wipe runny noses
- clean up the floor when the baby throws strained spinach
- clean ovens and grease traps and roasting pans
- empty the kitty box and scrape up the dog doo
- carry out the garbage
- pump out the bilges
- bury dead pets when they get run over in the street

I'd tell the graduates that when they can do these things, they will be adults. Some of the students might not want to go on at this point. But they may as well face the truth.

It can get even worse than the list suggests. My wife is a doctor, and I won't tell you what she tells me she has to do sometimes. I wish I didn't know. I feel ill at ease sometimes being around someone who does those things. And also proud.

A willingness to do your share of cleaning up the mess is a test. And taking out the garbage of this life is a condition of membership in community.

When you are a kid, you feel that if they really loved you, they wouldn't ever ask you to take out the garbage. When you join the ranks of the grown-ups, you take out the garbage because you love them. And by "them" I mean not only your own family, but the family of humankind.

The old cliché holds firm and true.

Being an adult *is* dirty work.

But someone has to do it.

heritage

BY
ANITA
SKEEN

driving south on route 60 at dawn he would say to me,
my chin hooked over the back of the front seat
a few inches from his ear,
thinking how the lines in the back
of his neck were like the deep gullies
that cut through the back hills,
a tense laugh in his voice
"there's where your old man puts in his time"

narrow pipes spit fire at the morning
as ovens cough up white-hot coke
rows of stacks, choking
belch out circles of thick breath
holding my nose, swallowing
even closing my eyes
does not help:
i still drown
in ammonia and smell
that same smell woven into the fiber
of his heavy wool shirts
it fills our house
when he enters each night
and moves with his hands as they
pass food at the supper table

in dreams i climb
thin ladders on those big tanks
my bones against their bones
my flesh freezing, weeping
in the winter cold
to toss my orange hat far up
far out above the webs of dark steel

Hades

BY

ROBERT

HILLES

y father was a coal miner and each day he returned home covered in what his labour produced. I don't know if he liked it underground we never talked about that. Every morning he would wake me with his coughing as he got ready for work. I would watch him from my bed as he sat at the table drinking his tea and looking straight in front of him as if his father was seated across from him. Sometimes he would speak quietly to his tea or hum a little when he couldn't find the words. I would turn over and listen to him with my eyes closed and I knew that a father was a sound in the morning someone who worked underground trying to find secrets there that he could bring home. My father's teeth were bad and they got worse each year and when he smiled nothing shone back from inside his mouth even his tongue was starting to turn black. And he would cough at night in his sleep as if he were answering back the gods that he found there underground. Sad, stooped-over gods who could not tell you anything about the world because they had been below too long. Gods he would carry home in his lunchbox and talk to them as if they were children that knew nothing of the world they inherited. He would tell me stories from the underground of boys who died in cave-ins before they had learned to use a razor. Once he was trapped for hours by a cave-in. He sang to himself to keep his spirits up and how he never thought of death only of what the sun felt like on an arm in the early afternoon. When they found him, he was covered head to toe in an inch of coal dust only his eyes and mouth visible in the darkness. One of his legs was crushed when he was yet a boy and he walked with a limp and stooped over most of the time even when standing out in the sun. He taught me how our hands can only make or change a small part of the world that underground people don't change just remember the outside better than most. Some coal miners finding their way out not with lights but following the draft from the surface. Some even worked in the dark to save their lights turning them on now and then to make sure that their work was right. My father had small hands and they were always black and even the food he ate was covered in coal dust and once and awhile he would have my mother cut his hair so that it was not in his way when he worked. I never asked him if he liked his job or if it was what he wanted. We have never shared our dreams or talked about what a father or son might only what a father and son can. To him work was underground a place so dark even your body was invisible to you. I never went below to find out what it was like too frightened that I might like it or that my father would stop being my father down there and become someone else. When I was old enough, I left town to go to school and never came back until he died. He was still young his lungs so full of coal dust there was nothing they could do to save him. The night before his funeral I paced the rooms of our small house trying to decide if I should go down the shaft just once. In a foolish way I thought that I might find him still alive down there happy in his underworld talking and laughing with his friends so happy that the sun and the rest of the world didn't matter anymore. But I knew all I would find there would be the darkness he fled into death. There would be nothing of his down there nothing but a faint chill dragged down from the surface. I couldn't face that or the images in my mind of him stooped over reaching into the darkness for another shovel full of coal another inch towards his own end. I didn't cry at the funeral just watched him being lowered into the earth and being covered like he was each day the earth draining his life slowly until now we offered it what was left and it did nothing remained silent as it had always been taking its own sweet time to reveal its secrets. It must have spoken to him and told him things he could not bring back to the surface. But he never spoke of it never let anything out took it with him back down this last time no longer able to fight his way back to the surface. I will always remember him as he came in the front door each day covered in black dust smiling and whistling knowing that for the next few hours he would be in the light. Even at night at least there were the stars overhead and now and then the moon looking so optimistic in the sky all by itself crossing the night sky like a promise from someone brave.

Fern Hill

BY

DYLAN

THOMAS

Now as I was young and easy under the apple boughs
About the lilting house and happy as the grass was green,
　　The night above the dingle starry,
　　　　Time let me hail and climb
　　Golden in the heydays of his eyes,
And honoured among wagons I was prince of the apple towns
And once below a time I lordly had the trees and leaves
　　　　Trail with daisies and barley
　　Down the rivers of the windfall light.

And I was green and carefree, famous among the barns
About the happy yard and singing as the farm was home,
　　In the sun that is young once only,
　　　　Time let me play and be
　　Golden in the mercy of his means,
And green and golden I was huntsman and herdsman, the calves
Sang to my horn, the foxes on the hills barked clear and cold,
　　　　And the sabbath rang slowly
　　In the pebbles of the holy streams.

All the sun long it was running, it was lovely, the hay
Fields high as the house, the tunes from the chimneys, it was air
    And playing, lovely and watery
        And fire green as grass.
    And nightly under the simple stars
As I rode to sleep the owls were bearing the farm away,
All the moon long I heard, blessed among stables, the nightjars
    Flying with the ricks, and the horses
        Flashing into the dark.

And then to awake, and the farm, like a wanderer white
With the dew, come back, the cock on his shoulder: it was all
    Shining, it was Adam and maiden,
        The sky gathered again
    And the sun grew round that very day.
So it must have been after the birth of the simple light
In the first, spinning place, the spellbound horses walking warm
    Out of the whinnying green stable
        On to the fields of praise.

And honoured among foxes and pheasants by the gay house
Under the new made clouds and happy as the heart was long,
    In the sun born over and over,
        I ran my heedless ways,
    My wishes raced through the house high hay
And nothing I cared, at my sky blue trades, that time allows
In all his tuneful turning so few and such morning songs
    Before the children green and golden
        Follow him out of grace,

Nothing I cared, in the lamb white days, that time would take me
Up to the swallow thronged loft by the shadow of my hand,
    In the moon that is always rising,
        Nor that riding to sleep
    I should hear him fly with the high fields
And wake to the farm forever fled from the childless land.
Oh as I was young and easy in the mercy of his means,
        Time held me green and dying
    Though I sang in my chains like the sea.

from

Wordstruck

～

BY

ROBERT

MACNEIL

O ut of the atmosphere of values every family breathes of what is good and what is bad, I knew that the sea was good. I took for granted that it built character to go to sea, to wrest your living from it, to respect it, to be in awe of its terrible powers, but to take it as a matter of course that you went down to it and did business with it. In our mythology, everything to do with the sea was clean and honourable work.

Awareness of the sea used to be far more common than it is today, when air travel has made the oceans seem puny and most people think of boats only for pleasure. Experience of the sea used to be central in the lives of the English-speaking peoples; and knowledge of oceans was vital to commerce, exploration, and conquest.

The sea was so familiar a part of Western life from the Elizabethans to the twentieth century that expressions relating to it became metaphors for activities on the land. Such expressions filled the language I heard or read in the books about the sea that I began devouring at twelve or thirteen.

Everybody depended on *his ship coming in.* They were *all in the same boat,* waiting till *the bitter end.* In everyday life, they would *back and fill,* or be *taken down a peg or two* if they didn't *know the ropes.*

They had to keep *a weather eye open* and give a stranger *a wide berth* if he was *bearing down on them* and they didn't like *the cut of his jib,* because he might be *armed to the teeth,* at least until he *showed his true colours* or *nailed his colours to the mast.* If he *spliced the main-brace* before *the sun was over the yardarm,* put too much *grog on the rocks* and *down the hatch,* got *three sheets to the wind* and *keeled over,* he might have to *trim his sails* and *pour oil on troubled waters* to get on an even keel, or risk being *keel-hauled.* If they *slacked off* or *rested on their oars, weren't pulling their own weight,* or *sailed too close to the wind,* someone might *lower the boom* and *take the wind out of their sails,* forcing them to *chart a new course. In the doldrums,* if they didn't *make headway* and were *dead in the water,* they might be *all at sea* and long for a *safe harbour,* because *time and tide wait for no man.* If *landlubbers shoved off* and ventured on the *high seas, come hell or high water,* where it wasn't all *plain sailing,* they'd have to *hit the decks* and *haul it* or be *half seas over* and even *pooped* before they could *drop anchor* or *barge in* to put their *port* side along-side the dock for the *longshoremen* to discharge cargo. If some *tar* lis-tened to too much *scuttlebutt* and talked *a lot of bilge,* they might *give him some leeway* or tell him to *pipe down* or put him in the *booby hatch* if he and the captain were *at loggerheads.* If a ship was *first-rate,* and the captain no *figurehead,* he'd have her *shipshape from stem to stern,* so *by and large* she'd get *a clean bill of health.* Then the *swab* could *clear the decks, stow it,* lower the *gangway,* don his *middy blouse* and *peajacket,* and, if he wasn't too *hard up,* go off *on his own hook* and see whether the *broad-beamed* lady pacing the *widow's walk* still liked him or was just a *fairweather friend....*

The sea was a destination to us. It was somewhere to go, for an outing, a walk. The only real place for the picnics that were a frequent entertain-ment were the long, empty beaches of Nova Scotia, still empty today. We did not sit on them much to sunbathe and only when very young played in the sand, building castles with moats for the rising tide to fill. The beaches had other purposes: to explore beyond the next headland and the next, learning to run over the rocks deftly, placing each foot uncon-sciously; to look for interesting shells; to skip flat stones; to gather drift-wood for a fire. My father was very good at starting fires in a circle of round beach stones close enough to balance a kettle or pot. Starting with a tent of bleached twigs, he had a big fire burning in a few minutes.

We did not go to the beaches only in nice weather. We went when we went. We enjoyed the beaches as often on grey, cloudy days with a fresh wind blowing as on days when the sand reflected a dazzling sun with no wind. More typically, there was wind and a strong lungful of breathtaking freshness tasting of iodine and seaweed clean enough to eat.

From my mother came the idea that going down to the sea repaired the spirit. That is where she walked when she was sad or worried or lonely for my father. If she had been crying, she came back composed; if she had left angry with us, she returned in good humour. So we naturally believed that there was a cleansing, purifying effect to be had; that letting the fresh wind blow through your mind and spirits as well as your hair and clothing purged black thoughts; that contemplating the ceaseless motion of the waves calmed a raging spirit.

The
Playground

BY
RAY
BRADBURY

A thousand times before and after his wife's death Mr. Charles Underhill ignored the Playground on his way to and from his commuters' limited train. He neither liked nor disliked the Playground; he hardly knew it existed.

But only this morning his sister Carol, who had occupied the empty space across the breakfast table from him each day for six months, quietly broached the subject.

"Jim's almost three years old now," she said. "So tomorrow I'm going to start him at the Playground."

At his office, he underlined a memorandum with black ink: *Look at Playground.*

That afternoon, the thunder of the train subsiding in his body, Underhill struck up through town on his usual path home, newspaper tucked crisply under arm to prevent reading himself past the park. So it was, at five-ten in the late day, that he came to the cool iron fence and the open gate of the Playground, and stood for a long, long time, frozen there, gazing in at it all....

At first there seemed absolutely nothing whatever to see. And then as he adjusted his attention outward from his usual interior monologue, the scene before him, a gray, blurred television image, came to a slow focus. Primarily, he was aware of dim voices, faint underwater cries emerging from a series of vague streaks and zigzag lines and shadows. Then, as if someone had kicked the machine, screams jumped at him in full throat, visions leaped clear. Now he saw the children! They were dashing across the Playground meadow, fighting, pummeling, scratching, falling, every wound bleeding or about to bleed or freshly caked over. A dozen cats thrown among sleeping dogs could not have shrieked as loud. With incredible clarity, Mr. Underhill saw the tiniest cuts and scabs on knees and faces.

He weathered the first blast of sound, blinking. His nostrils took over when his eyes and ears retired in panic.

He sniffed the cutting odors of salve, raw adhesive, camphor, and pink Mercurochrome, so strong it lay bitter on his tongue. An iodine wind blew through the steel fence wires which glinted dully in the gray light of the overcast day. The rushing children were hell cut loose in a vast pinball table, colliding, and banging, a totaling of hits and misses, thrusts and plungings to a grand and as yet unforeseen total of brutalities.

And was he mistaken or was the light within the Playground of a peculiar intensity? Every child seemed to possess four shadows: one dark, three faint penumbras which made it strategically impossible to tell which way their swift bodies were racing until they bashed their targets. Yes, the oblique, pressing light made the Playground seem deep, far away, and remote from his touching. Or perhaps its was the hard steel wire fence, not unlike those barriers in zoos, beyond which *anything* might happen.

A pen of misery, thought Underhill. Why do children insist on making life horrible for each other? Oh, the continual torture. He heard himself sigh with immense relief. Thank God, childhood was over and done for him. No more pinchings, bruisings, senseless passions and shattered dreams.

A gust of wind tore the paper from his hand. He ran after it down the Playground steps. Clutching the paper, he retreated hastily. For in that one brief instant, stranded in the Playground's atmosphere, he had felt his hat grow too large; his coat too cumbersome; his belt too loose; his shoes too big; he had felt like a small boy playing businessman in his father's clothes; and the gate behind him had loomed impossibly tall, while the sky pressed a huge weight of grayness at his eyes, and the scent of iodine, like a tiger's breath exhaled upon him, blew his hair. He tripped and almost fell, running back.

He stood outside the Playground, like someone who has just emerged, in shock, from a terrible cold sea.

"Hello, Charlie!"

He heard the voice and turned to see who had called him. There on top of a metal slide, a boy of some nine years was waving. "Hello, Charlie...!"

Mr. Charles Underhill raised a hand. But I don't *know* that boy, he thought. And why should he call me by my first name?

The boy was smiling high in the misty air, and now, jostled by other yelling children, rushed shrieking down the slide.

Underhill stood bemused by what he saw. Now the Playground was an immense iron industry whose sole products were pain, sadism, and sorrow. If you watched half an hour there wasn't a face in the entire enclosure that didn't wince, cry, redden with anger, pale with fear, one moment or another. Really! Who said Childhood was the best time of life? when in reality it was the most terrible, the most merciless era, the barbaric time when there were no police to protect you, only parents preoccupied with themselves and their taller world. No, if he had his way, he touched the cold fence with one hand, they' d nail a new sign here: TORQUEMADA'S GREEN.

And as for that boy, the one who had called out to him, who was he? There was something familiar there, perhaps in the hidden bones, an echo of some old friend; probably the son of a successfully ulcered father.

So this is the Playground where my son will play, thought Mr. Underhill. So this is it.

Hanging his hat in the hall, checking his lean image in the watery mirror, Underhill felt wintry and tired. When his sister appeared, and his son came tapping on mouse feet, he greeted them with something less than full attention. The boy clambered thinly over him, playing King of the Hill. And the father, fixing his gaze to the end of the cigar he was slowly lighting, finally cleared his throat and said, "I've been thinking about that Playground, Carol."

"I'm taking Jim over tomorrow," said his sister.

"Not really? *That* Playground?"

His mind rebelled. The smell and look of the place were still vivid. That writhing world with its atmosphere of cuts and beaten noses, the air as full of pain as a dentist's office, and those horrid ticktacktoes and frightening hopscotches under his feet as he picked up his newspaper, horrid and frightening for no reason he could see.

"What's wrong with *that* Playground?" asked Carol.

"Have you seen it?" He paused in confusion. "Damn it, I mean, the children there. It's a Black Hole."

"All the children are from well-to-do families."

"Well, they shove and push like little Gestapos," said Underhill. "It'd be like sending a boy to a flour mill to be crushed into meal by a couple of two-ton grinders! Every time I think of Jim in that barbaric pit, I freeze!"

"You know very well it's the only convenient park for miles around."

"I don't care about that. All I care is I saw a dozen kinds of bats and clubs and air guns. By the end of the first day, Jim would be in splinters. They'd have him barbecued, with an orange in his mouth."

She was beginning to laugh. "How you exaggerate."

"I'm serious!"

"You can't live Jim's life for him. He has to learn the hard way. He's got to take a little beating and beat others up; boys are like that."

"I don't *like* boys like that."

"It's the happiest time of life."

"Nonsense. I used to look back on childhood with great nostalgia. But now I realize I was a sentimental fool. It was nothing but screaming and running in a nightmare and coming home drenched with terror, from head to foot. If I could possibly save Jim from that, I would."

"That's impractical and, thank God, impossible."

"I won't have him near that place, I tell you. I'll have him grow up a neurotic recluse first."

"Charlie!"

"I will. Those little beasts, you should've seen them! Jim's *my* son, he is; he's not yours, remember." He felt the boy's thin legs about his shoulders, the boy's delicate fingers rumpling his hair. "I won't have him butchered."

"He'll get it in school. Better to let him get a little shoving about now, when he's three, so he's prepared for it."

"I've thought of that, too." Mr. Underhill held fiercely to his son's ankles which dangled like warm, thin sausages on either lapel. "I might even get a private tutor for him."

"Oh, Charles!"

They did not speak during dinner.

After dinner, he took Jim for a brief walk while his sister was washing the dishes. They strolled past the Playground under the dim street lamps. It was a cooling September night, with the first dry spice of autumn in it. Next week, and the children would be raked in off the fields like so many leaves and set to burning in the schools, using their fire and energy for more constructive purposes. But they would be here after school, ramming about, making projectiles of themselves, crashing and exploding, leaving wakes of misery behind every miniature war.

"Want to go in," said Jim, leaning against the high wire fence, watching the late-playing children beat each other and run.

"No, Jim, you don't want that."

"Play," said Jim, his eyes glassy with fascination as he saw a large boy kick a small boy and the small boy kick a smaller boy to even things up.

"Play, Daddy."

"Come along, Jim, you'll never get in that mess if *I* can help it." Underhill tugged the small arm firmly.

"I want to play." Jim was beginning to blubber now. His eyes were melting out of his face and his face was becoming a wrinkled orange of colour.

Some of the children heard the crying and glanced over. Underhill had the terrible sense of watching a den of foxes suddenly startled and looking up from the white, hairy ruin of a dead rabbit. The mean yellow-glass eyes, the conical chins, the sharp white teeth, the dreadful wiry hair, the brambly sweaters, the iron-coloured hands covered with a day's battle stains. Their breath moved out to him, dark licorice and mint and Juicy Fruit so sickeningly sweet, so combined as to twist his stomach. And over this hot mustard smell of someone tolerating an early chest cold; the greasy stink of flesh smeared with hot camphorous salves cooking under a flannel sheath. All these cloying and somehow depressing odors of pencils, chalk, grass and slate-board erasers, real or imagined, summoned old memory in an instant. Popcorn mortared their teeth, and green jelly showed in their sucking, blowing nostrils. God! God!

They saw Jim, and he was new to them. They said not a word, but as Jim cried louder and Underhill, by main force, dragged him like a cement bag along the walk, the children followed with their glowing eyes. Underhill felt like pushing his fist at them and crying, "You little beasts, you won't get *my* son!"

And then, with beautiful irrelevance, the boy at the top of the blue metal slide, so high he seemed almost in a mist, far away, the boy with the somehow familiar face, called out to him, waving and waving.

"Hello, Charlie...!"

Underhill paused and Jim stopped crying.

"See you later, Charlie...!"

And the face of the boy way up there on that high and very lonely slide, was suddenly like the face of Thomas Marshall, an old business friend who lived just around the block, but whom he hadn't seen in months.

"See you later, Charlie."

Later, later? What did the fool boy mean?

"I know *you,* Charlie!" called the boy. "Hi!"

"What?" gasped Underhill.

"Tomorrow night, Charlie, hey!" And the boy fell off the slide and lay choking for breath, face like a white cheese from the fall, while children jumped him and tumbled over.

Underhill stood undecided for five seconds or more, until Jim thought to cry again and then, with the golden fox eyes upon them, in the first chill of autumn, he dragged Jim all the way home.

The next afternoon Mr. Underhill finished at the office early and took the three o'clock train, arriving out in Green Town at three twenty-five, in plenty of time to drink in the brisk rays of the autumnal sun. Strange how one day it is suddenly autumn, he thought. One day it is summer and the next, how could you measure or tell it? Something about the temperature or smell? Or the sediment of age knocked loose from your bones during the night and circulating in your blood and heart, giving you a slight tremble and a chill? A year older, a year dying, was *that* it?

He walked up toward the Playground, planning the future. It seemed you did more planning in autumn than any other season. This had to do with dying, perhaps. You thought of death and you automatically planned. Well, then, there was to be a tutor for Jim, *that* was positive; none of those horrible schools for him. It would pinch the bank account a bit, but Jim would at least grow up a happy boy. They would pick and choose his friends. Any slam-bang bullies would be thrown out as soon as they so much as touched Jim. And as for this Playground? Completely out of the question!

"Oh, hello, Charles."

He looked up suddenly. Before him, at the entrance to the wire enclosure, stood his sister. He noted instantly that she called him Charles, instead of Charlie. Last night's unpleasantness had not quite evaporated. "Carol, what're you doing *here*?"

She flushed guiltily and glanced in through the fence.

"You didn't!" he cried.

His eyes sought among the scrabbling, running, screaming children. "Do you mean to say...?"

His sister nodded, half amused. "I thought I'd bring him early—"

"Before I got home, so I wouldn't know is *that* it?"

That was it.

"Good God, Carol, where *is* he?"

"I just came to see."

"You mean you left him there all afternoon?"

"Just for five minutes while I shopped."

"And you *left* him. Good God!" Underhill seized her wrist. "Well, come on, find him, get him out of there!"

They peered in together past the wire to where a dozen boys charged about, girls slapped each other, and a squabbling heap of children took turns at getting off, making a quick run, and crashing one against another.

"That's where he is, I *know* it!" said Underhill.

Just then, across the field, sobbing and wailing, Jim ran, six boys after him. He fell, got up, ran, fell again, shrieking, and the boys behind shot beans through metal blowers.

"I'll stuff those blowers up their noses!" said Underhill. "Run, Jim! Run!"

Jim made it to the gate. Underhill caught him. It was like catching a rumpled, drenched wad of material. Jim's nose was bleeding, his pants were ripped, he was covered with grime.

"*There's* your Playground," said Underhill, on his knees, staring up from his son, holding him, at his sister. "*There* are your sweet, happy innocents, your well-to-do piddling Fascists! Let me catch this boy here again and there'll be hell to pay. Come on, Jim. All right, you little bastards, get back there!" he shouted.

"We didn't do nothing," said the children.

"What's the world coming to?" Underhill questioned the universe.

"Hi! Charlie!" said the strange boy, standing to one side. He waved casually and smiled.

"Who's that?" asked Carol.

"How in hell do *I* know?" said Underhill.

"Be seeing you, Charlie. So long," called the boy, fading off.

Underhill marched his sister and his son home.

"Take your hand off my elbow!" said Carol.

He was trembling; absolutely, continually trembling with rage when he got to bed. He had tried some coffee, but nothing stopped it. He wanted to beat their pulpy little brains out, those gross Cruikshank children; yes, that phrase fit them, those fox-fiend, melancholy Cruikshank children, with all the guile and poison and slyness in their cold faces. In the name of all that was decent, what manner of child was this new generation! A bunch of cutters and hangers and bangers, a drove of bleeding, moronic, thumbscrewers, with the sewage of neglect running in their veins? He lay violently jerking his head from one side of his hot pillow to the other, and at last got up and lit a cigarette, but it wasn't enough. He and Carol had had a huge battle when they got home. He had yelled at her and she had yelled back, peacock and peahen shrieking in a wilderness where law and order were insanities laughed at and quite forgotten.

He was ashamed. You didn't fight violence with violence, not if you were a gentleman. You talked very calmly. But Carol didn't give you a chance, damn it! She wanted the boy put in a vise and squashed. She wanted him reamed and punctured and given the laying on of hands. To be beaten from playground to kindergarten, to grammar school, to junior high, to high school. If he was lucky, in high school, the beatings and sadisms would refine themselves, the sea of blood and spittle would drain back down the shore of years and Jim would be left upon the edge of maturity, with God knows what outlook to the future, with a desire, perhaps, to be a wolf among wolves, a dog among dogs, a fiend among fiends. But there was enough of that in the world, already. The very thought of the next ten or fifteen years of torture was enough to make Mr. Underhill cringe; he felt his own flesh impaled with BB shot, stung, burned, fisted, scrounged, twisted, violated, and bruised. He quivered, like a jelly-fish hurled violently into a concrete mixer. Jim would never survive it. Jim was too delicate for this horror.

Underhill walked in the midnight rooms of his house thinking of all this, of himself, of the son, the Playground, the fear; there was no part of it he did not touch and turn over with his mind. How much, he asked himself, how much of this is being alone, how much due to Ann's dying, how much to my need, and how much is the reality of the Playground itself, and the children? How much rational and how much nonsense? He twitched the delicate weights upon the scale and watched the indicator glide and fix and glide again, back and forth, softly, between midnight and dawn, between black and white, between raw sanity and naked insanity. He should not hold so tight, he should let his hands drop away from the boy. And yet—there was no hour that looking into Jim's small face he did not see Ann there, in the eyes, in the mouth, in the turn of the nostrils, in the warm breathing, in the glow of blood moving just under the thin shell of flesh. I have a right, he thought, to be afraid. I have every right. When you have two precious bits of porcelain and one is broken and the other, the last one, remains, where can you find the time to be objective, to be immensely calm, to be anything else but concerned?

No, he thought, walking slowly in the hall, there seems to be nothing I can do except go on being afraid and being afraid of being afraid.

"You needn't prowl the house all night," his sister called from her bed, as she heard him pass her open door. "You needn't be childish. I'm sorry if I seem dictatorial or cold. But you've got to make up your mind. Jim simply cannot have a private tutor. Ann would have wanted him to go to a regular school. And he's got to go back to that Playground tomorrow and keep going back until he's learned to stand on his own two feet and until he's familiar to all the children; then they won't pick on him so much."

Underhill said nothing. He got dressed quietly, in the dark, and, downstairs, opened the front door. It was about five minutes to midnight as he walked swiftly down the street in the shadows of the tall elms and oaks and maples, trying to outdistance his rage and outrage. He knew Carol was right, of course. This was the world, you lived in it, you accepted it. But that was the very trouble! He had been through the mill already, he knew what it was to be a boy among lions; his own childhood had come rushing back to him in the last few hours, a time of terror and violence, and now he could not bear to think of Jim's going through it all, those long years, especially if you were a delicate child, through no fault of your own, your bones thin, your face pale, what could you expect but to be harried and chased?

He stopped by the Playground which was still lit by one great overhead lamp. The gate was locked for the night, but that one light remained on until twelve. He wanted to tear the contemptible place down, rip up the steel fences, obliterate the slides, and say to the children, "Go home! Play in your back yards!"

How ingenious, the cold, deep Playground. You never knew where anyone lived. The boy who knocked your teeth out, who was *he*? Nobody knew. Where did he live? Nobody knew. How to find him? Nobody knew. Why, you could come here one day, beat the living tar out of some smaller child, and run on the next day to some *other* Playground. They would never find you. From Playground to Playground, you could take your criminal tricks, with everyone forgetting you, since they never knew you. You could return to this Playground a month later, and if the little child whose teeth you knocked out was there and recognized you, you could deny it. "No, I'm not the one. Must be some other kid. This is my first time here! No, not me!" And when his back is turned, knock him over. And run off down nameless streets, a nameless person.

What can I possibly do? thought Underhill. Carol's been more than generous with her time; she's been good for Jim, no doubt of it. A lot of the love she would have put into a marriage has gone to him this year. I can't fight her forever on this, and I can't tell her to leave. Perhaps moving to the country might help. No, no, impossible; the money. But I can't leave Jim here, either.

"Hello, Charlie," said a quiet voice.

Underhill snapped about. Inside the Playground fence, seated in the dirt, making diagrams with one finger in the cool dust, was the solemn nine-year-old boy. He didn't glance up. He said "Hello, Charlie," just sitting there, easily, in that world beyond the hard steel fence.

Underhill said, "How do you know my name?"

"I know it." The boy crossed his legs, comfortably, smiling quietly. "You're having lots of trouble."

"How'd you get in there so late? Who are you?"

"My name's Marshall."

"Of course! Tom Marshall's son Tommy. I *thought* you looked familiar."

"More familiar than you think." The boy laughed gently.

"How's your father, Tommy?"

"Have you seen him lately?" the boy asked.

"On the street, briefly, two months ago."

"How did he look?"

"What?"

"How did Mr. Marshall *look*?" asked the boy. It seemed strange he refused to say "my father."

"He looked all right. Why?"

"I guess he's happy," said the boy. Underhill saw the boy's arms and legs and they were covered with scabs and scratches.

"Aren't you going home, Tommy?"

"I sneaked out to see you. I just knew you'd come. You're afraid."

Mr. Underhill didn't know what to say.

"Those little monsters," he said at last.

"Maybe I can help you." The boy made a dust triangle.

It was ridiculous. "How?"

"You'd give anything, wouldn't you, if you could spare Jim all this? You'd trade places with him if you could?"

Mr. Underhill nodded, frozen.

"Well, you come down here tomorrow afternoon at four. Then I can help you."

"How do you mean, help?"

"I can't tell you outright," said the boy. "It has to do with the Playground. Any place where there's lots of evil, that makes power. You can feel it, can't you?"

A kind of warm wind stirred off the bare field under the one high light. Underhill shivered. Yes, even now, at midnight, the Playground seemed evil, for it was used for evil things. "Are all Playgrounds like this?"

"Some. Maybe this is the only one like this. Maybe it's just how *you* look at it, Charlie. Things *are* what you *want* them to be. A lot of people think this is a *swell* Playground. They're right, too. It's how you look at it, maybe. What I wanted to say, though, is that Tom Marshall was like you. He worried about Tommy Marshall and the Playground and the kids, too. He wanted to save Tommy the trouble and the hurt, also."

This business of talking about people as if they were remote made Mr. Underhill uncomfortable.

"So we made a bargain," said the boy.

"Who with?"

"With the Playground, I guess, or whoever runs it."

"Who runs it?"

"I've never seen him. There's an office over there under the grandstand. A light burns in it all night. It's a bright, blue light, kind of funny. There's a desk there with no papers on it and an empty chair. The sign says MANAGER, but nobody ever sees the man."

"He must be around."

"That's right," said the boy. "Or I wouldn't be where I am, and someone else wouldn't be where they are."

"You certainly talk grown-up."

The boy was pleased. "Do you want to know who I really am? I'm not Tommy Marshall. I'm Tom Marshall, the father. He sat there in the dust, not moving, late at night, under the high and faraway light, with the late wind blowing his shirt collar gently under his chin, blowing the cool dust. "I'm Tom Marshall, the father. I know it'll be hard for you to believe. But it *is* true. I was afraid for Tommy. I was the way you are now about Jim. So I made this deal with the Playground. Oh, there are others who did the same, here. If you look close, you'll see them among the other children, by the expression in their eyes."

Underhill blinked. "You'd better run home to bed."

"You want to believe me. You want it to be true. I saw your eyes just then. If you could trade places with Jim, you would. You'd like to save him all that torture, let him be in your place, grown-up, the real work over and done."

"Any decent parent sympathizes with his children."

"You, more than most. You feel every bite and kick. Well, you come here tomorrow. You can make a deal, too."

"Trade places?" It was an incredible, an amusing, but an oddly satisfying thought. "What would I have to do?"

"Just make up your mind."

Underhill tried to make his next question sound very casual, a joke, but his mind was in a rage again. "What would I pay?"

"Nothing. You'd just have to play in the Playground."

"All day?"

"And go to school, of course."

"And grow up again?"

"Yes, and grow up again. Be here at four tomorrow afternoon."

"I have to work in the city tomorrow."

"Tomorrow," said the boy.

"You'd better get home to bed, Tommy."

"My name is *Tom* Marshall." The boy sat there.

The Playground lights went out.

Mr. Underhill and his sister did not speak at breakfast. He usually phoned her at noon to chat about this or that, but he did not phone. But at one-thirty, after a bad lunch, he dialled the house number. When Carol answered he hung up. Five minutes later he phoned again.

"Charlie, was that you called five minutes ago?"

"Yes," he said.

"I thought I heard you breathing before you hung up. What'd you call about, dear?" She was being sensible again.

"Oh, just called."

"It's been a bad two days, hasn't it? You *do* see what I mean, don't you, Charlie? Jim *must* go to the playground and get a few knocks."

"A few knocks, yes."

He saw the blood and the hungry foxes and the torn rabbits.

"And learn to give and take," she was saying, "and fight if he has to."

"Fight if he has to," he murmured.

"I knew you'd come around."

"Around," he said. "You're right. No way out. He must be sacrificed."

"Oh, Charlie, you *are* odd."

He cleared his throat. "Well, that's settled."

"Yes."

I wonder what it would be like? he thought.

"Everything else okay?" he asked the phone.

He thought of the diagrams in the dust, the boy seated there with the hidden bones in his face.

"Yes," she said.

"I've been thinking," he said.

"Speak up."

"I'll be home at three," he said slowly, piercing out the words like a man hit in the stomach, gasping for breath. "We'll take a walk, you and Jim and I," he said, eyes shut.

"Wonderful!"

"To the Playground," he said and hung up.

It was really autumn now, the real chill, the real snap, overnight the trees burnt red and snapped free of their leaves, which spiraled about Mr. Underhill's face as he walked up the front steps, and there were Carol and Jim bundled up against the sharp wind, waiting for him.

"Hello!" they cried to one another, with much embracing and kissing. "There's Jim down there!" "There's Daddy up there!" They laughed and he felt paralyzed and in terror of the late day. It was almost four. He looked at the leaden sky, which might pour down molten silver any moment, a sky of lava and soot and a wet wind blowing out of it. He held his sister's arm very tightly as they walked. "Aren't you friendly, though?" she smiled.

"It's ridiculous, of course," he said, thinking of something else.

"What?"

They were at the Playground gate.

"Hello, Charlie. Hi!" Far away, atop the monstrous slide stood the Marshall boy, waving, not smiling now.

"You wait here," said Mr. Underhill to his sister. "I'll only be a moment. I'll just take Jim in."

"All right."

He grasped the small boy's hand. "Here we go, Jim. Stick close to Daddy."

They stepped down the hard concrete steps and stood in the flat dust. Before them, in a magical sequence, stood the diagrams, the gigantic ticktacktoes, the monstrous hopscotches, the amazing numerals and triangles and oblongs the children had scrabbled in the incredible dust.

The sky blew a huge wind upon him and he was shivering. He grasped the little boy's hand still tighter and turned to his sister. "Good-by," he said. For he was believing it. He was in the Playground and believing it, and it was for the best. Nothing too good for Jim! Nothing at all in this outrageous world! And now his sister was laughing back at him, "Charlie, you idiot!"

Then they were running, running across the dirt Playground floor, at the bottom of a stony sea that pressed and blew upon them. Now Jim was crying, "Daddy, Daddy!" and the children racing to meet them, the boy on the slide yelling, the ticktacktoe and hopscotchers whirling, a sense of bodiless terror gripping him, but he knew what he must do and what must be done and what would happen. Far across the field footballs sailed, baseballs whizzed, bats flew, fists flashed up, and the door of the Manager's office stood open, the desk empty, the seat empty, a lone light burning over it.

Underhill stumbled, shut his eyes and fell, crying out, his body clenched by a hot pain, mouthing strange words, everything in turmoil.

"There you are, Jim," said a voice.

And he was climbing, climbing, eyes closed, climbing metal-ringing ladder rungs, screaming, yelling, his throat raw.

Mr. Underhill opened his eyes.

He was on top of the slide. The gigantic, blue metal slide which seemed ten thousand feet high. Children crushed at his back, children beat him to go on, to slide. Slide!

And he looked, and there, going off across the field, was a man in a black overcoat. And there, at the gate, was a woman waving and the man standing there with the woman, both of them looking in at him, waving, and their voices calling, "Have a good time! Have a good time, Jim!"

He screamed. He looked at his hands, in a panic of realization. The small hands, the thin hands. He looked at the earth far below. He felt his nose bleeding and there was the Marshall boy next to him. "Hi!" cried the other, and bashed him in the mouth. "Only twelve years here!" cried the other in the uproar.

Twelve years! thought Mr. Underhill, trapped. And time is different to children. A year is like ten years. No, not twelve years of childhood ahead of him, but a century, a century of *this*.

"Slide!"

Behind him the stink of Musterole, Vicks VapoRub, peanuts, chewed hot tar, spearmint gum and blue fountain-pen ink, the smell of kite twine and of glycerin soap, a pumpkin smell of Halloween and a papier-mâché fragrance of skull masks, and the smell of dry scabs, as he was pinched, pummeled, shoved. Fists rose and fell, he saw the fox faces and beyond, at the fence, the man and woman standing there, waving. He shrieked, he covered his face, he felt himself pushed, bleeding, to the rim of nothingness. Headfirst, he careened down the slide, screeching, with ten thousand monsters behind. One thought jumped through his mind a moment before he hit bottom in a nauseous mound of claws.

This is hell, he thought, this is *hell!*

And no one in the hot, milling heap contradicted him.

Part-time Work: Challenge or Handicap in High School?

BY

ALLEN

PANZERI

Kirsten Andersen, a Grade 12 student at Harry Ainlay high school, needs more skills than a juggler to keep her busy life in balance. Maintaining her honor-roll grades and playing basketball while working between 10 and 15 hours a week at a fast-food restaurant give the 17-year-old all she can handle.

"It gets to be pretty stressful and sometimes it's hard to keep up with your school work because you're so tired," she said. "But you have to learn to manage your time as best you can. So far it hasn't been too bad."

Andersen's situation is not unusual. She is just one of thousands of students who hold down a part-time job while going to school.

This was not always viewed with alarm. In the 1970s, educators saw part-time work as a way to ease the transition from school to the labor market, and to emphasize the relevance of the school curriculum.

But now educators are wondering if the rush of students to largely low-wage, unskilled jobs in the service sector interferes with the education they need to join the highly skilled workforce of the future.

"It's one of those situations where it can be good for some students and it cannot be good for some other students," said Queen Elizabeth principal Wilma Bayko. "It boils down to a balance more than anything else. I think the research says that working fewer than 20 hours a week for some students is OK, but when they work more than 20 hours a week, it tends to interfere with their schooling."

According to figures from the

Edmonton Public School Board, 53 per cent of the students surveyed at Harry Ainlay high school and 54 per cent at Queen Elizabeth have part-time jobs.

Across Canada, 39 per cent of high school students worked during the 1990 school year. Of the Harry Ainlay students surveyed 11 per cent worked less than 10 hours a week, 28 per cent worked between 10 and 20 hours, and 61 per cent worked more than 20.

At Queen Elizabeth, 19 per cent worked less than 10 hours, 54 per cent worked between 10 and 20, and 26 per cent worked more than 20.

Statistics Canada figures from 1990 indicate students from 15 to 24 worked an average of 13.8 hours a week, with 33 per cent working less than 10. Fifty per cent worked between 10 and 20, and 25 per cent worked more than 20.

The problem for educators is that research so far has been sketchy and inconclusive, and the relationship between work and school is not simple. While there are some positive benefits in learning management skills and instilling a work ethic, some studies indicate that grades fall and the time spent on homework decreases if students work more than 20 hours a week.

Opinion is sharply divided.

"The reason it's kind of mixed is that I think it actually helps some kids," said Eastglen principal El Probert. "You can see some kids grow a lot from it. They accept their responsibilities better and they manage their time better. So those are some of the pluses.

"But by the same token, other students get distracted by it all. It's a hard one to call. It's almost an individualistic thing. You can't make a blanket statement to say that it's all bad or all good."

The reasons for taking part-time jobs also vary widely. Of the Ainlay students, 54 per cent said the main reason for working was to "drive a car," while 15 per cent said the job paid for necessities.

At Queen Elizabeth, 30 per cent said the part-time job paid for necessities, while only six per cent were working to afford a car.

Pressure to wear the latest clothes and have the latest devices is also a big factor, said Probert.

Andersen works to pay some of the costs associated with playing basketball. Her parents pay the yearly fee that covers transportation. She covers her own expenses when the team travels.

"If you play sports, it can be very expensive for your parents to dish out all that money," she said. "So I feel I should contribute part of it, because I'm the one who is actually playing the sport."

Grade 11 student Chris Maclure, 16, works part-time at a fast-food restaurant to pay for hockey and the occasional ski trip. His parents pay about half the $800 to $1000 it costs to play hockey every year; he pays the rest. Because activities cost so much and prices rise every year, Maclure says there's additional pressure on students to work so they can contribute. "Without the job, I wouldn't be able to play hockey."

Grade 12 student Andre Morgan works about 15 hours a week, mostly on the weekend, as a bus-boy at a restaurant. He figures that working any more than one night a week is too much. "If you want to prepare for school and your exams, it's not a good idea to work more than that."

Child Workers Risking Death

BY

LESLIE

PAPP

housands of youngsters across Ontario are risking their education, health, and even their lives to work hard hours on our farms and in our cities.

While condemning child labor in the Third World, many Canadians have been blind to the dangerous practices in our own backyard.

In rural Ontario, children as young as 7 are put to work driving tractors and doing other hazardous chores. With at least 30 dead in the last dozen years, they're paying a heavy price.

"Kids in the prime of life are being ripped apart by machinery," says Steve Zronik of Ontario's Farm Safety Association.

In urban Ontario, teenagers are lining up to work long hours in fast-food restaurants, gas stations and convenience stores. They risk being scarred for life by hot-oil burns, crushed in machinery they don't know how to use, and falling victim to violent crime.

Some youths work more than 30 hours a week—until 1 or 2 a.m. some days—arriving at school late, or not at all. Many are too weary to concentrate on their classwork even when they manage to attend. Experts warn that thousands of students are sacrificing their grades, and future prospects, in the quest for a minimum wage.

"Work is now a large part of student life, but a lot of students are losing something very valuable to them—their education," says Judy Bromley, principal at Sir Robert Borden high school in Scarborough.

Society offers little protection for its youngest workers. Under the law, a youngster of any age can drive a tractor or do other farm labor. There's no limit to how many hours an employer can demand from a teenage employee. And there's no cap on how late students can work.

"To be honest, the old child labor issue hasn't really been raised in this country," Labor Minister Bob Mackenzie said in an interview.

"I haven't picked it up as an issue of concern," he said, expressing an attitude shared by most Ontarians. "I just haven't turned my thoughts to it."

Meanwhile, children work across this province. And all too often children suffer and children die.

Teen workers hit by hot-oil burns

The burned tissue on Steve Prince's right leg will always remind him of the dangers of working at a fast-food outlet. Prince was seared in a hot-oil accident while working as a 16-year-old at a fast-food restaurant three years ago. Now he's scarred for life.

"I've tried different specialists, but there's nothing they can do," he says. "It's hit me hard."

And he isn't alone. Workers' Compensation Board statistics show that 88 employees, 15 and 16 years old, suffered serious on-the-job burns or scalds in Ontario in 1992. More than 600

in this age group were compensated for major injuries, including 12 who endured amputations, and 159 who had major cuts or punctures.

Burns, cuts, sprains and falls are major hazards facing the thousands of teenagers working in fast-food outlets across Ontario, safety experts warn. Kitchens can be a crowded and hectic environment. And risk increases when the labor force is young, part-time, working late, and with limited training.

"The fast-food industry is the new sweat-shop," said Dr. Philip Landrigan, director of occupational medicine at Mount Sinai Hospital, in New York, and an expert on child labor injuries.

"There are some horrible burns," said Cathy Walker, national health and safety director for the Canadian Auto Workers, a union representing about 3000 fast-food workers across the country. "It's kids training kids at a lot of these places," Walker said. "And you've got kids who have been at school all day working until quite late at night. That's when a lot of injuries happen."

Prince had the misfortune to be walking across a wet, freshly mopped floor while hot oil was being removed from a restaurant fryer. Three knee-high containers of the scorching liquid were on the floor when Prince walked by and was bumped by a bustling fellow employee. As he slipped and lost his balance, his right leg plunged into one container. He fell, knocking over the other two and spilling their contents across the floor where he lay.

Shocked fellow employees were unable to help as the oil spread and Prince screamed. "Everyone stood and watched me fry," he says.

Prince received burns to his back, legs and arms but managed to keep those to a minimum by quickly stripping off his oil-soaked clothing. The foot that was in a container, however, was deeply seared around the ankle and lower shin. "The doctors told me I was lucky I didn't lose my toes," Prince says, now finishing high school and working part-time as an apartment building assistant superintendent. "It still hurts psychologically. I'm marked for life."

But at least Prince still has a life. Sixteen-year-old Luis Cunha wasn't as lucky. He died March 12, 1992, while trying to clear jammed cardboard in a machine used to compact boxes for recycling. When the machine unexpectedly started, Cunha's head and neck were pressed between a wire safety gate and a hydraulic plate. "Now I'll never have my brother," says Helen Cunha, 17, Luis' sister. "I'll be an only child for the rest of my life."

When he died Luis was working part-time for a cleaning company hired by a department store. Testimony at a subsequent hearing showed that none of Cunha's supervisors had read the instruction manual that came with the compactor, and the youth was given only a quick lesson in its use. Supervisors also ignored a label on the machine advising that it was not to be used by anyone under 18....

An unknown number of teenagers are victims of violence as they tend convenience store cash registers, dispense doughnuts, or pump gasoline late into the night. Metro police say they don't keep statistics on the age and occupation of victims. But an examination of police incident reports, over a recent three-week period, shows Metro teens were robbed or beaten on the job at the rate of two a week.

One of them, a 16-year-old Scarborough gas station attendant, was hit on the hand with a club and repeatedly pummeled to the ground in a brutal Halloween night assault. He was back on the job a few days later, but his middle-aged partner had both arms shattered when a gang of 15 youths attacked a Danforth Rd. gas station. "They've got pins holding his bones together," observes the youth, catching his breath as he scrambles from one car to another to pump gas.

Troubled by the attack, he now works two seven-hour shifts weekly instead of the six nights a week he served before Halloween.

He drives his father's van to work, fearing gang members might recognize his red Camaro in the parking lot. And he pleads that his name not be published. "I don't want them knowing where I live."

But he continues with the job. "Money is money," he says with a shrug. "You gotta have money."

When Work and Its Labours Feel Good

BY

LIANNE CARLEY

It was still dark out. Somebody was singing at the top of his voice and beating on a makeshift drum. Ah yes, the 5 a.m. wake-up call.

We'd begun our third week of construction at Boca Brava, a sandstrip located on the Pacific coast in the south of Costa Rica.

Never built a wall before? How about a roof? Neither had I. But, you learn quickly. By theorizing, improvising and compromising, the team eventually created an impressive structure that would act as a dining room for the local school. The construction itself was a slow process. Materials were often unavailable. And it was difficult getting them to the boca since high tide occurred only every 12 hours, so they could be transported by boat through crocodile infested waterways. Patience was an asset.

We spent the first couple of days on the boca setting up camp...latrines and a wall, clearing a tenting site, building showers. We were starting from scratch, which is why our weekend of training near Calgary paid off. The minute we'd arrived there, staff at Youth Challenge International (YCI) confiscated all watches, tents, emergency food like chocolate bars and trail mix. They threw us every curve they could in the 48 hours we were together. Now, we were glad they had.

It's no easy task to cook with unfamiliar food, make do with limited facilities and please a dozen hungry young people. Ironically, although lunch and dinner were always interesting culinary creations, oatmeal seemed to be a standard morning meal, perhaps due more to convenience than popular demand.

There we were, 43 Canadians, 20 Costa Ricans, 8 Australians, 6 Guyanese, 2 Russians, all with YCI. Life on Boca Brava was a satisfying balance of work and play. On Christmas Day, José, a local boy, took six of us clam digging in a nearby swamp. Although the participants' haul of 10 clams (four of which turned out to be an inedible variety) paled in comparison to José's 93, it was surely one of the most fascinating Christmas mornings any of us had ever experienced.

It was still dark out. The Howler monkeys were screaming in the distance. Somebody's watch alarm started to beep. It was 5:30 a.m. and we were to meet American biologist Ken Clark in half an hour. It was only day three of our scientific research project in the Monte Verde Cloudforest Reserve in the northwestern part of Costa Rica and already we'd learned so much about the ecology of the region. This morning we were going to be collecting cloudwater samples and recording relative humidity and wind speed. Later, back at the lab we'd analyse samples and discuss the results. Ken always took time to explain exactly what we were doing, and

why. It was still dark out. The chattering cows in the barn below us constantly reminded us that we were now calling their house our home. Suddenly somebody shouted "Breakfast!" followed by the Spanish version, "Desayuno!" Surprise, surprise, oatmeal for the 75th morning in a row.

Only two more weeks left in our program. We were now in Palmera, an isolated community located in the east just west of Limon. The medical centre begun by a different YCI group the previous month was ours to finish. Walls still had to be constructed and painted. The ceiling still had to be installed. The plumbing was still to be done. The catch? Official opening of the clinic was in a week and a half. Complete everything in 10 days? A challenge, but not impossible. Working day and night, we were able to have the building ready on schedule. On opening day, 12 doctors and hundreds of people showed up for medical attention. Our long work hours were important for these people.

Still dark out. Winter in Canada. Stars out by 4:30 in the afternoon. Program over and I'm back in Vancouver, realizing how much I've learned. I've seen three different areas of Costa

Rica, worked in a tropical rain-forest, built up a working knowledge of Spanish and discovered 101 different uses for oatmeal!

I've learned some pretty amazing things about myself... my tolerances, intolerances, my abilities and my limits.

It's Just a Matter of Time

BY

HELEN WILKINSON

~

n *The Intimate History of Humanity,* French academic Theodore Zeldin notes that women and young people are leading the movement to win back control of our time from the demands of jobs and bosses. For women time has always been at a premium—more so as growing numbers of women work as well as mother and nurture—and the younger generation has seen the costs of too much work and too little time in the lives of their parents.

His insights reinforce research we are carrying out at Demos, an independent British public policy think tank, on the changing values of today's young people. One central finding of Demos' report, *Generation X and the New Work Ethic,* is that control over one's time is the third most important career goal of British young people today. (The first, traditionally enough, is money; the second is the chance to use their brains.)

The report shows that young people want to work but don't want to overwork; they reject the "time bravado" culture of the past, with its workaholic worship of long hours at the job, in favor of a "life friendly" work culture.

Demos' report also reveals generational tensions between the baby boomer generation, who are now managers, and the young workers they are recruiting or managing. Managers lament the incapacity of today's youth to work hard. One particular issue that seems to vex baby-boom bosses is the realization that the old-style corporate loyalty of the past does not resonate with the younger generation. The assumption among young professionals is that old-style employment relationships simply cannot be trusted today. Young people will constantly ask of an employer, "What have you got to teach me?" They believe that security nowadays comes from the transferability of one's skills to other jobs rather than from advancement in hierarchically managed organizations. Economic uncertainty has bred self-reliance among this younger generation,

Managers also frequently complain that younger employees have erratic timekeeping. They don't understand young people's desire to work from home or late at night rather than according to the fixed corporate hours.

For their part, Generation Xers are critical of the sloppiness of their managers, their laziness for failing to keep up with technology, their reliance on secretaries and personal assistants rather than the Internet, and, crucially, their failure to use time efficiently. Many young people criticize their managers for their "make-work" rather than "real-work" mentality. They have no sympathy with the way their elders spend time in meetings rather than getting down to the job at hand.

What are the reasons for this generational divide in today's offices? Maybe it has something to do with the fact that young professionals in their twenties are the first generation to have been socialized into a work culture where insecurity is the order of the day and where there are no jobs for life.

With a few exceptions, business has been slow to recognize the problems of the "time bravado" culture—the stress that is caused and created by a culture of presenteeism (the workaholic equivalent of absenteeism; you are always at your desk no matter how little you accomplish).

An increasing number of young workers, especially women, have decided to opt out of traditional workplaces. In the United States and increasingly in the United Kingdom, there is no shortage of young women setting up their own businesses: They're no longer prepared to wait for companies who have not been able to change their work culture fast enough. The implications of this attempt to regain control of their time is clear. Women and young people want work to be judged not on input but on output, no longer on the site where work is done, but on how well work is done.

On this point, Theodore Zeldin senses that history might be on our side, since we're now moving away from industrialism and the time culture that was necessary for assembly-line work: "There is a new sensitivity to the texture of time, to what makes it flow smoothly, agreeably, sensuously. People do dream of enjoying their work by doing it at a rhythm which suits them and varying their rhythm for different occupations. This notion of personal rhythm was what the industrial revolution attacked and tried to destroy."

We must ask what needs to be done to speed up the process of breaking free from the tyranny of too little time. For a start, the workplace should allow time out for college courses, community volunteering, and sabbaticals. The sabbatical is close to my heart. After five years working as a researcher and producer of TV documentaries, I needed time to recharge my batteries, work in a different environment surrounded by different people and learn different skills. I was lucky enough to have a broad-minded manager who could see that this was a necessary stage for me. I was granted a sabbatical last year.

I read Zeldin's history of the sabbatical with delight. He writes: "The weekend is only one half of the Sabbath. God also instructed the Jews to make a sabbatical holiday every seven years, in which they should stop tilling the land, cancel debts, and release their slaves." He goes on to predict that "the sabbatical year may become a human right demanded in the 21st century.... Since individuals are increasingly unhappy about wasting talents which they cannot use in their jobs, the sabbatical year might have a future, offering an opportunity to change direction, or simply to do what busy people do not have the time to do, namely, think or take a long promenade." It was precisely in my seventh year of working after college that I felt the need to take a break.

Zeldin goes on to argue for a government role in making sabbaticals compulsory—just as it once decreed the 40-hour week. If sabbaticals are not made compulsory, then taking one might be read as disloyalty and lack of commitment. After all, the paradox of our society is that we have enforced idleness for some (a growing 14.4 percent of British society) and overwork for many.

Somewhere in the middle lies a balance. Women have known the need for it for many years and young people perhaps are now the wisest of us all.

Employability Skills Profile:

The Critical Skills Required of the Canadian Workforce

ACADEMIC SKILLS

Those skills which provide the basic foundation to get, keep and progress on a job and to achieve the best results

- -

Canadian employers need a person who can:

Communicate

◆ Understand and speak the languages in which business is conducted

◆ Listen to understand and learn

◆ Read, comprehend and use written materials, including graphs, charts and displays

◆ Write effectively in the languages in which business is conducted

Think

◆ Think critically and act logically to evaluate situations, solve problems and make decisions

◆ Understand and solve problems involving mathematics and use the results

◆ Use technology, instruments, tools and information systems effectively

◆ Access and apply specialized knowledge from various fields (e.g., skilled trades, technology, physical sciences, arts and social sciences)

Learn

◆ Continue to learn for life

PERSONAL MANAGEMENT SKILLS

The combination of skills, attitudes and behaviours required to get, keep and progress on a job and to achieve the best results

Canadian employers need a person who can demonstrate:

Positive Attitudes and Behaviours

◆ Self-esteem and confidence

◆ Honesty, integrity and personal ethics

◆ A positive attitude toward learning, growth and personal health

◆ Initiative, energy and persistence to get the job done

Responsibility

◆ The ability to set goals and priorities in work and personal life

◆ The ability to plan and manage time, money and other resources to achieve goals

◆ Accountability for actions taken

Adaptability

◆ A positive attitude toward change

◆ Recognition of and respect for people's diversity and individual differences

◆ The ability to identify and suggest new ideas to get the job done—creativity

TEAMWORK SKILLS

Those skills needed to work with others on a job and to achieve the best results

Canadian employers need a person who can:

Work with Others

◆ Understand and contribute to the organization's goals

◆ Understand and work within the culture of the group

◆ Plan and make decisions with others and support the outcomes

◆ Respect the thoughts and opinions of others in the group

◆ Exercise "give and take" to achieve group results

◆ Seek a team approach as appropriate

◆ Lead when appropriate, mobilizing the group for high performance

Parachute

BY

LENRIE

PETERS

Parachute men say
The first jump
Takes the breath away
Feet in the air disturbs
Till you get used to it

Solid ground
Is now where you left it
As you plunge down
Perhaps head first
As you listen to
Your arteries talking
You learn to sustain hope

Suddenly you are only
Holding an open umbrella
In a windy place
As the warm earth
Reaches out to you
Reassures you
The vibrating interim is over

You try to land
Where green grass yields
And carry your pack
Across the fields

The violent arrival
Puts out the joint
Earth has nowhere to go
You are at the starting point

Jumping across worlds
In condensed time
After the awkward fall
We are always at the starting point.

Eight Days
a Week

B Y
L I N D A
L E W I S

Last summer, when Nora Spinks spent a week camping with her husband and son, she spotted one of the most telling, and perhaps troubling, signs of the times—and it wasn't clear-cut trees, or dead fish along the beach. Every day, she hiked out to the entrance of the provincial park to use one of four pay phones. "I had to phone my office," she recalls. "And I couldn't believe it—*I had to line up.*" Like Spinks, all those other vacationers were checking in with the office. And who knows how many other concerned campers were calling in from the privacy of their own tents, via cellular. "People are afraid to be away from the workplace for too long," says Spinks, president of Canadian Work and Family Services. "They're afraid they'll miss something...God forbid they take a week's holiday."

Look around you and it won't take long to confirm that we have entered a new age of overwork. Canadians—those who have jobs, that is—are working harder, faster and longer. A survey of 27 000 Canadian employees found that we're working an average of 45 hours per week; 18% of us are working 60 hours or more. And close to half of all managers and professionals interviewed reported spending several additional hours performing job-related duties at home. As well, Statistics Canada reports that more than half a million of us are moonlighting. If, as Benjamin Franklin said, time is money, then Canadians today are thoroughly impoverished.

The bewildering thing is, *this wasn't supposed to happen.* "Twenty years ago, experts predicted we could all work a four-day workweek and we could all retire at age 38," says Robert Glossop, director of programs and research at the Vanier Institute of the Family in Ottawa. "Fifteen years ago, people studied 'Leisurology'—I don't know what the graduates in leisurology are doing these days." Now, instead of stopping to smell the roses in what was supposed to be the Great Decade of Downtime, we're too busy smelling the coffee that's brewing in the wee hours at the office.

"In the '80s, we thought that in the '90s we would have more time with our spouse or family. In the '90s, people are having less time," says Dr. Warren Shepell, a Toronto psychologist who runs a national company specializing in employee assistance programs. "In the '80s, we expected we'd have more fun. The reality in the '90s is, we're having less fun. Most frustrating of all, in the '80s, we expected a higher disposable income. In the '90s, we have less disposable income."

Five years ago, when "success" and "status" were the buzzwords, overwork had a certain cachet. At the end of the long evening at the office was a dinner at the latest trendy pesto bar; at the end of the tough project was the promise of a promotion. Nowadays, Canadians aren't working to get ahead on the fast track; we're working simply to stay *on* the track. And thanks to downsizing, many employees are now saddled with a workload that has doubled or tripled.

On top of the new productivity pressures is anticipatory stress: the anticipation, real or imagined, that you're next in line for the pink slip. This creates what Linda Duxbury, a business professor at Carleton University in Ottawa, calls the conspiracy of silence. "People are having a tremendous problem speaking out, because they're afraid they'll be the next to go," says Duxbury, one of four professors who conducted a study called *Balancing Work and Family: A Study of the Canadian Work Force.* "*Work* has to be the priority because if it isn't, people feel they'll lose their job."

As the study found, overwork is democratic. It doesn't matter how old you are, what industry you're in, or even where you live. "The average employed American has seen his or her working hours increased by the equivalent of one month a year," writes Harvard associate professor Juliet Schor in her 1991 book *The Overworked American.* "Weekly schedules are getting longer, by about one hour per week. This is the first sustained peacetime increase in weekly hours during the 20th century.... Half the population now say they have too little time for their families."

No one knows the stress, feels it, more than parents: "Work-family conflict is really work-parenting conflict," report the authors of the Balancing Work and Family study. "If both mother and father are working (as is the case in 70% of our sample), someone still has to find time to attend medical appointments, shop, cook, etc."

Working mothers are still the ones doing the second shift: "Women are especially stressed out, because first they look after their kids, then their spouse, *then* themselves," says Duxbury. A 1991 survey done by Price Waterhouse and economist Earl Berger in the Canada Health Monitor found that, including housework and child care, the total working time of employed mothers averages about 60 hours a week. Schor estimates that figure is closer to 65 hours a week—and between 70 and 80 hours for mothers of young children.

Perhaps the most dire evidence of all is an informal statistic noted by Duxbury. Her research team conducted in-depth interviews with 500 couples about how they cope. "We had five female MA or PhD students conducting the interviews," she says. "At the end, they all said they're not going to have kids."

The time famine, says Spinks, is devastating to children as well as their parents. "If you're working 50 hours-plus, probably you're doing some of that work at home," she notes. "Kids are hearing, 'Shush, go away, I'm busy.' People aren't taking the time to tell the kids that it's not their fault, that the reason they can't get to swimming lessons is that mom and dad don't have the time to get them there."

As the Vanier Institute's Glossop notes, things on the home front have deteriorated to the point where "you get counsellors suggesting that families hold regular meetings." Back in those not-so-distant days when people studied leisurology, we never thought it would come to this; where we will find ourselves in another 10 or 15 years is just as difficult to predict. In the meantime, as the following profiles attest, people are finding their own ways to cope with the realities of the overloaded '90s.

Hugh Robinson

When Hugh Robinson recently met with an old friend in a bar after work, he couldn't wait to catch up on things. They hadn't had time to chat in close to a year. So when a woman sitting nearby started eavesdropping on their conversation and then jumped in, Robinson checked his watch with irritation. He wanted to leave by 7:30 so he could kiss his one-year-old daughter, Caitlin, goodnight. "I resented that we didn't have time to talk about personal things," Robinson says. "I really have no time anymore just to meet occasionally with a friend and talk about how things are."

He doesn't want to sound like a whiner. As a project manager in children's services with Ontario's Ministry of Community and Social Services, he has a window onto many people far worse off than he. Still, Robinson, 38, does regret that the demands of modern living have given him less time for simple pleasures like conversation. "What are my day-to-day priorities? I've got to keep my job, make enough money, and spend time with my family. What loses out is having enough time to think about important issues, like the environment, or politics." So does spending time as a twosome with his wife, Karen, a product manager at a health-care firm.

Tacked onto Robinson's 50-hour-plus workweek is a 40-minute commute to downtown Toronto from Milton, Ont. He leaves home at 5:40 a.m. (so he can try to fit in a workout at the Y) and returns at about 7 p.m. (His wife, who works closer to home, drives the baby to and from the sitter. Robinson tries to do the other duties, like making lunch and getting Caitlin's bottles ready.)

For Robinson, proposed cuts and layoffs in the public service are a new concern. But he's also looking on the bright side: if he ends up having to take several government-mandated unpaid days off a year, he will have a bit more time to spend with his widowed mother, and perhaps to squeeze in a golf game. Mostly he simply wants to be there for his daughter. "I've made a choice to have a child in a world, where, on my bad days, I've got to really question it." And he wonders, "Are we going to be the kind of role models that she deserves?"

Hugh Robinson's Typical Day
Wake up. Get Caitlin's bag ready for the babysitter, put out diapers for diaper service pickup, get ready for work.

Drive to Toronto.

Work out at the Y, go to the bank, dry cleaners, run other errands.

Work through lunch, perhaps pick up groceries, perhaps stop off and see Mother for a few minutes. Drive home.

Arrive home, spend time with Caitlin (already fed by Karen). Put her to bed.

"Free time"—Eat dinner, do some things around the house, read the paper, finish up some work on the computer, make phone calls, talk to Karen.

Prepare Caitlin's lunch/bottles/laundry for the next day. Make own lunch and Karen's lunch.

Pat Macdonald

The interview is scheduled for 5:30, but at 3:30, Pat Macdonald calls in a panic to postpone it. "I'm running really late. I have to get this project finished...I'm just really stressed out here. Oh, boy, if you saw me right now...."

By the evening, sipping a Diet Coke in her landscaped back yard, Macdonald seems the embodiment of poise. Still, she admits she's in the midst of "a heavy stress time"—sometimes going for weeks without a day off, often working at home from 9:30 to 11, getting her husband to bring her three- and six-year-old sons to her office on weekends so she can see them. They don't mind—after all, she's vice-president of marketing and sales at Canada's Wonderland, the mammoth amusement park north of Toronto.

Macdonald, who is 42, belongs to a generation in the midst of some serious navel gazing. "You say to yourself, 'What is it I really want to be? What is it I'm working for?'" But she considers herself lucky: "I'm still working because I choose to. There's a certain level of power one feels when you're working because you *want* to versus because you *have* to."

Macdonald doesn't *feel* overworked, largely because she and her husband, Ian, a partner in a merchant bank, have established certain coping mechanisms. They schedule a family ski trip every March, no matter what. In the morning, Macdonald doesn't leave the house until 8:30, and she sometimes uses her long drive to work to make calls on the car phone. And because she can afford to employ a full-time live-in nanny, who oversees most of the household duties, Macdonald doesn't have to worry about mundane details like the breakfast dishes.

"We decided a long time ago that if it came down to doing something ourselves or going to the Yellow Pages and getting someone else to do it—painting a bedroom, plumbing—we'd get someone else," she says. "We called it buying our way through a crisis."

What is lacking is personal time. "I don't have any time to pamper myself. Going and getting a haircut—now I've got to cram it in. It's not relaxing and fun any more.

"I think I have to become a bit more selfish," says Macdonald. In the meantime, her boys are calling her from inside the house, wanting attention. In a couple of hours she'll tuck them into their beds—and then tuck into her briefcase. All in a day's work.

Pat Macdonald's Typical Day
7-7:15 a.m. Wake up, have coffee, read paper.
7:15-8:15 a.m. Have breakfast. Get kids dressed.
8:30-9 a.m. Drop off Ian (older son) at school. Drive to work.
1-1:15 p.m. Eat lunch, usually at desk.
6:15-6:40 p.m. Drive home from work.
6:45-8:30 p.m. Change clothes. Play with kids. Make dinner for self and husband. Give kids dessert.
8:30-9 p.m. Bathe kids. Put them to bed.
9-9:30 p.m. Eat dinner with husband. Clean up.
9:30-11 p.m. Open mail from work.
11-11:30 p.m. Lights out.

Debbie Clark

Greeting potential customers in front of her booth at a Toronto women's networking event, Debbie Clark epitomizes the three C's of the '90s businesswoman: cool, calm and connected. But, just a short time ago, while rushing in on the highway from Oshawa, she was talking rapidly into a microcassette recorder, reminding herself of people she had to call, things she had to finish, problems she had to deal with. Clark, 28, recently took her first vacation in four years. Last year, she put in 14-hour days throughout her pregnancy—and went back to work two weeks after her baby was born.

She didn't realize anything was wrong until she saw her family doctor about all the headaches she was having, and they had a long talk about stress. Now, a couple of months later, Clark is getting counselling every week for what she calls "the progressive effects of workaholism." Her family doctor gave her stress management exercises, persuaded her to include one hour of leisure time a day on her to-do list, and "made me see that if I keep going at this pace, I'm going to have a heart attack by age 35."

Clark has always had a strong work ethic. "I wanted to go to college very badly," she says, "and in order to save for a college education,

I had to work really hard." In 1991, Clark was a contract employee in General Motors' customer assistance division when she decided to seek freedom and fortune as an entrepreneur. Together with her husband, Derrick, a firefighter, she got a second mortgage on their house and bought a Mail Boxes Etc. franchise (offering postal, communication and business services). In two years, she says proudly, she has tripled the gross income of the franchise; recently she bought the area rights for the region stretching from Belleville to Pickering, Ontario.

Like many self-employed people, Clark found that running her own shop gave her less freedom, not more. "When we first began the business, it was do or die," she says. "Our first year-end was April 30 and the baby was due May 1. I was doing payroll, advertising, getting accounts ready. I had no choice—I had to be there."

Now, she admits, "I don't think we have to keep going at this pace; we could probably cut it in half and still do well." But she and her husband find it difficult to ease up on themselves. "Some days he's at work for 10 hours, and then we're in the office at home till 2 in the morning. Then he gets up and goes to work at 7:30." Still, watching their 17-month-old daughter, Paige, grow up has prompted the couple to take a good look at what their lives have become. "Part of my self-help is to sit down with my husband and discuss all of this," says Clark. "We're both taking steps at learning how to do nothing."

Debbie Clark's Typical Day
6 a.m. Paige wakes up. Give her a bottle.
7 a.m. Get ready for work. Get Paige's bag ready for the babysitter.
7:30 a.m. Feed, dress and play with Paige.
8:30 a.m. Take Paige to the babysitter. Drive to work.
8:45 a.m. Arrive at the store.
Noon. No lunch; perhaps munch on a muffin while working.
4 p.m. Leave store to do business banking.
5:45 p.m. Fill up briefcase to bring home. Pick up Paige from babysitter. Get home and start cooking dinner.
7-7:30 p.m. Eat dinner with husband and daughter.
7:30-9:30 p.m. Bathe and play with Paige.
9:30 p.m. Put Paige to bed.
10 p.m. Throw in some laundry. Write out to-do list for the morning.
11 p.m.-2 a.m. Work in the home office, together with Derrick.
2 a.m. Go to bed.

When the Job Sneaks Into Your Dreams

BY

**CALEB
SOLOMON**

All alone in the dining room of Chez Panisse in Berkeley, Calif., the restaurant's famous chef, Alice Waters, has to attend to hungry customers all by herself. The waiters have vanished; busboys are nowhere to be seen. Rushing to the kitchen, Ms. Waters finds herself alone. No sous-chef. No kitchen help. And, worst of all, no food.

If that sounds like a restaurateur's worst dream, that's just what it is—a recurring job-related nightmare that Ms. Waters says disturbs her sleep every few nights. "There's this horrifying moment of realization that the food is not ready. It's not ready, and all those hungry people are out there," she says, in a tremulous voice.

Cajun chef Paul Prudhomme has his own version of the Restaurant Dream, but in his the kitchen air is as thick as jelly. "You're pushing it away, trying to make things happen, and you can't."

Dreams, it seems, are an occupational hazard for professionals and wage slaves of all sorts. Dentists, for example, don't just cause nightmares; they have them. So do architects and zookeepers. "Your dream life parallels your working life," says Rita Dwyer, a director of the Association for the Study of Dreams, a nonprofit group of sleep specialists in Vienna, Va.

Although scientific interest in dreams is at its peak—and books on their supposed meaning abound—little study has been done on job-relatedness. Now, with companies laying off employees—and the job market scary, even during daylight hours—workers and therapists are starting to compare notes about things that go bump in the night.

Milton Kramer, director of the Sleep Disorders Center of Bethesda Hospital in Cincinnati, says he has dreamed a dream common among directors. An angry patient quits therapy. "On the way out, he points out that my pants have fallen down," says Dr. Kramer, a psychiatrist. He adds an interpretation: "It's my fear of my patient exposing me and my incompetence."

Job dreams often are a far cry from the heroic daydreams of James Thurber's Walter Mitty. They are more on the order of the well-nigh universal Test Anxiety Dream that many people have for years after graduation day. At the age of 77, Nobel-prize winning biologist Francis Crick still dreams of taking an exam for which "you're not prepared and you fail."

No wonder aerobics instructors' nights are filled with missing sneakers; cracks in the stage swallow up musicians' sheet music; architects toss and turn about mistaken measurements that cause buildings to topple.

Andrea Conway, an acrobat on tour with Quebec's Cirque du Soleil, has a common performance nightmare: "I'm on stage and, all of a sudden, the show is different and I don't know what I'm doing there."

Of course, not every job inspires common dreams, or even variations on a theme. Economists, it is said, don't dream a collective dream or have any particular incubus.

Bill Gilmer, a senior economist with the Federal Reserve Bank in Houston, says maybe that is because economists aren't creative enough to conjure one up. "We just sort of [leave the job] at night and start out again the next morning."

Bernard Weinstein, an economist at the University of North Texas, says he dreams of everything but the dismal science. "I dream of what I really want to be," he says, "a stand-up comedian or a jazz musician."

Dreams feed on physical activity and props. Zoos are rich in the material that the brain can twist and turn into dreamscapes. In the dreams of Valerie Thompson, a keeper at the San Diego Zoo, the animals are in jeopardy. Koalas escape, antelopes make suicidal leaps and giraffes are mortally wounded. After a night in this violent bestiary, Ms. Thompson is exhausted. She says, "You feel like you never left work." And she feels cheated: "This was supposed to be my time to escape."

The zoological nightmares of Norberto Castro have him sweating over the human visitors. Mr.

Castro, an assistant curator at the Audubon Institute in New Orleans, dreams of a four-tonne elephant named Sneezy running amok. Mr. Castro wakes up relieved that the elephant isn't actually rampaging—but the image persists in his waking thoughts.

The architects' dreams one hears about are reminiscent of a Disney animated feature, *Aladdin* maybe. Measurements on blueprints come alive. "There are numbers dancing along," says Donald Rattner, of the New York firm Ferguson Murray & Shamamian, Architects. In a recent dream, the baseboards of a house put on a show by banging against a kitchen cabinet.

Kenneth Newberry, who helped design George and Barbara Bush's new house in Houston for the firm Eubanks Bohnn, says his floor plans sometimes get out of whack in the night. "In the dreams, the numbers don't add up."

Both architects say they also experience euphoric flying dreams. Mr. Newberry, his arms spread wide, meets clients aloft (though never the Bushes). "I love it when I wake up and I've been flying."

The pleasant work dream is the exception, experts say.

Real-estate broker Wendy Sarasohn of the Corcoran Group in New York dreamed that Kevin Costner becomes a client of hers. He picks her up in a limousine. He brings along his actor friend Don Johnson, who wants to purchase a place, too. Both buy penthouses and swoop Ms. Sarasohn off to Hollywood to become a movie star. "They have the perfect part for me," she says.

Dentists' nightmares tend to involve pain—their own as well as patients'. Arnold Gelfand, a New Orleans dentist, says he sees phobic faces in the night. "We're in a profession where there's a high degree of anxiety among certain people."

Baltimore dentist Harvey Solomon says, "That kind of patient can ruin your day." He has bad dreams, too, about the scaredy-cats: "You can't even anesthetize dream patients because their adrenalin floats out their ears."

The sleep of some writers is filled with monsters of a particularly vicious sort, who practise subtle tortures—and worse. Catherine Bowman, a New York poet, dreams she is walking nervously down a dark street. Suddenly a gang of marauders jumps from a corner and stabs her repeatedly in the right arm, the one she writes with. "Their faces are hidden," she says, "but they are editors."

When You Reach 65

BY
JOHN
KETTLE

My father, who was a bit ahead of his time, didn't want to retire at 65 and was not all that keen on quitting when, under some pressure from my mother, he did finally get out at 75.

It was a small firm and he was his own boss, so it hadn't been that hard for him to stay on. He relished the work, he liked most of the people he did business with, he enjoyed going up to the financial heart of England, the City of London, each day. In some ways the lifestyle, the office, the restaurant where he lunched, all had something of the character of a club.

If you work for Amalgamated Gigantic Inc. you may not feel the same way. But more and more people work for small companies. Close to a quarter of all employees today are in companies where the payroll is fewer than 20. Almost half are in companies with less than 100. Not one big happy family, necessarily, but far from that cog-on-the-wheel feeling big factories can give.

There are quite a lot of people like my father, who would like to keep on working past their 65th birthday, don't feel old at 65, and wouldn't know what to do with all that spare time. A few have gone to court to make their employers keep them on. Something like 10 per cent of men and 3 per cent of women over 65 are still working, and you have to assume that most of them are not doing it just for the money.

Ironically, because of corporate downsizing there are now more people complaining about early retirement. One calculation suggests that by 1992 between 100 000 and 200 000 people aged 55 to 64 were in premature retirement. That's a lot of people to fling out of the labour force, and their number is growing. You can't go down to the gym or the pub or the mall without running into someone complaining bitterly that they're not ready for retirement yet but here they are, turned out to pasture because the company downsized or went south.

Obviously there are lots of people who have burned out after decades on the assembly line or down the mine or selling shoes and who just can't wait to retire and put their feet up. The unions bargained hard to get early-retirement packages for their veteran members long before management came in with an offer they couldn't refuse.

Work is changing, though. There are fewer workers today for whom work means breaking their bodies in an endless battle with unyielding matter. That's partly because industrial jobs are disappearing and service jobs are increasing, partly because technology takes on more of the strain of industrial work. Today there are many for whom work is one of the more interesting things in their lives. Despite the bad rap service work gets, some of the most exciting jobs in the world are in services: media jobs, research, teaching, counselling. A growing number are not ready to retire at 65, let alone 55 or 60.

All this might be just a minor trend but for one thing. In the mid-1960s, when the Canada Pension Plan was introduced, people over 65 represented slightly more than 7 per cent of the population. Today they are nearly 12 per cent, and when the peak of the big postwar generation hits pensionable age, around 2025, they will be 20 per cent.

Instead of six working-age people for each one of pensionable age, there will be only three workers to support each pensioner. But CPP benefits and old-age pensions are paid out of current revenue, not investment. So only a few alternatives are open: higher contributions and taxes, lower benefits, or bankruptcy.

Or the age of retirement could be increased.

This is the solution the United States has decided on. Soon Americans won't be able to collect their old-age pension until they hit 67. No one has said the retirement age will continue to rise, but common sense says it probably will. And it could well do so here.

History doesn't often present two trends that converge to joint advantage, but this looks like one such occasion. More people are saying 65 isn't old any more and they would like to keep on working. The economy is telling us we can no longer afford retirement at 65. Two reasons for doing one thing. So don't be surprised if the next federal government decides to raise the retirement age.

You may not be sorry either.

Choosing Our Future

BY

JEREMY

RIFKIN

The year is 2045.

Life for most Americans is quite different today from what it was half a century ago. Perhaps the greatest visible change is the diminishing role of the economic marketplace in day-to-day affairs. Now that we are deep into the Information Age, most of the world's goods and services are produced in nearly workerless factories and marketed by virtual companies run by a small team of entrepreneurs and highly trained professionals. Sophisticated computers, robots, and state-of-the-art telecommunications technologies have replaced the "worker" of the industrial era. Less than 20 percent of the adult population works full time.

Most Americans receive their economic livelihood, in the form of voucher payments, from their local governing body in return for community service work in non-profit organizations. The vouchers are financed by the imposition of a value-added tax on high-tech goods and services.

Their projects run the gamut from helping take care of children and the elderly to working in preventive health programs, local art galleries, park maintenance, history projects, adult education, community gardens, and neighborhood sports teams as well as religious and political activities. Interestingly enough, the kind of nurturing and community-building skills that characterize work in the volunteer sector are the least vulnerable to replacement by computers, robots, and telecommunications technology. While market-oriented tasks—even highly technical and professional jobs—are often reducible to digitization and computerization, caring tasks that require intimate relationships between people are far too complex and difficult to be attended to by high-tech software. In the Post-Market Era, these are the high-status jobs. Because the productivity gains resulting from technological advances have been broadly distributed among all Americans, people's work—whether in community service or private business—takes up fewer than five hours a day, leaving more time for family, friends, personal projects, and relaxation. Some of the wealth from the high-tech revolution is also being shared with people in developing nations.

The values of the market economy that so dominated the industrial era have steadily given way to a new ethos based on personal transformation, community participation, and global responsibility. The older market system reinforced a materialist vision glorifying production and efficiency as the chief means of advancing happiness. As long as people's primary identification was with the market economy, the vision of unlimited personal consumption continued to influence most people's behavior. Americans thought of themselves first and foremost as "consumers" not as neighbors or citizens.

As more and more human beings were freed up from formal work in the market economy and began doing community service in the social economy, the values of community began to gain dominance across America and around the world. In preparation for a career in the social economy, children learn at home and in schools the value of helping others and of strengthening neighborhood and community bonds. While children spend part of their school time deep in cyberspace and virtual reality, they are expected to spend the remainder of their school experience in "real time," meeting people in their communities, helping create a more humane and ecologically sustainable society. Hands-on community service has become an integral part of the school experience. Youngsters help out in senior centers, animal shelters, environmental cleanup projects, and countless other neighborhood programs. They are prepared for a full life, not simply for a job. The emphasis on personal participation with others in the community is seen as a necessary antidote to the increasingly impersonal interaction generated by new computer and telecommunication technologies.

The transition to a Post-Market Era has not been easy. Corporate leaders and other vested interests fought the shift to a social economy every step of the way, particularly in the first decades of the 21st century. Nonetheless, support for post-market social policies continued to grow as more and more people were marginalized by the workings of the market economy. Although some opposition continues to this day from critics clinging to the values of the 20th-century market ethos, most Americans have adjusted well to the new Post-Market Era, enjoying the freedom that comes with less work in the marketplace.

Song of the
Accountant

BY

DOUG

ELVES

I count amphorae;
I keep track of jugs of olive oil, honey, grain and wine;
of spears, chariots, greaves and helmets.

I have also counted cattle, horses
and the fields that nurture them.

I've even counted people:
slaves the heady essence of whose work is in the wine;
serfs who keep their breakfasts while I buy their suppers, and
wage labourers who sell their grain to buy it back as supper.

I count it all and turn it into gold.
I am the original alchemist.
My magic has been imitated,
essayed but never equalled.
As long as I match it somewhere with a Credit,
I can Debit anything I like.
From Revenue to Asset, Asset to Equity,
the livelihoods of masses roll across my palm;
and I count them, assign them to the ledgers,
post, adjust, balance, close and summarize.

Opportunity for graft? Fraud?
Perhaps, but what I covet most
I can never embezzle:
I yearn for the giving unaware,
the rhythmic integrity of labour.
Produce and gather,
produce, refine, and gather,
produce, refine, adapt and gather
simply for the joy of doing what one cannot help but do.

And so I keep accounts
on hard, clay tablets, on parchment and on floppy disks.
I measure this one's work, that one's enterprise;
and should the profit fall to an interloper wielding spear and laws,
so much the better.
To such a one I rank among the labourers giving unaware,
and share their dignity.

The Carpenter

BY
PATRICK
LANE

The gentle fears he tells me of being
afraid to climb back down each day
from the top of the unfinished building.
He says: I'm getting old
and wish each morning when I arrive
I could beat into shape
a scaffold to take me higher
but the wood I'd need
is still growing on the hills
the nails raw red with rust
still changing shape in bluffs
somewhere north of my mind.

I've hung over this city like a bird
and seen it change from shacks to towers.
It's not that I'm afraid
but sometimes when I'm alone up here
and know I can't get higher
I think I'll just walk off the edge
and either fall or fly

and then he laughs
so that his plum-bob goes awry
and single strokes the spikes into the joists
pushing the floor another level higher
like a hawk who every year adds levels to his nest
until he's risen above the tree he builds on
and alone lifts off into the wind
beating his wings like nails into the sky.

The Yeoman of the Garbage

BY

ANTHONY JENKINS

olid Waste Management Division meets solid citizen at curbside at 7:27 a.m. We're the garbagemen, gliding down from the backstep of rear-packer No. 467 at the first "call" of a 1000-call, 12-tonne-a-man workday. We're in South Kingsway, a West Toronto district full of stately homes and arboreal arcades. The resident walking toward us has a fixed, strained smile as he waddles down his driveway. He's trying to keep a bulging, brown garbage can away from his BMW and his neatly pressed dress shirt.

We heave his weekly household waste into the hopper without curiosity and with an easy exchange of pleasantries: "Good morning, how's it going?" "Not too bad, boss. Have a good day."

"This is not science," says Mike Hearty, standing on the back step of the garbage truck. "We don't dwell on it, just get it in the hole." But the job is much more than that. It is dirty, dangerous, sometimes difficult and usually unappreciated....

A dozen years ago, all refuse went into the dump. Now garbage trucks proffer their contents to "sanitary landfill sites." Waste is classified as recyclables—yard waste (lawn clippings), toxic liquids and white metal/furniture (stoves, couches)—and the largest category, "solid household waste."

The sorting of the garbage—garbagemen don't bother with the bureaucratic niceties of "waste" and "landfill sites"—is supposed to be done by the public, but Frank Canestraro, manager of collection services for Etobicoke's Waste Management Division, says "People forget. Once it's in a green bag, it's garbage. Some people are conscientious, others use the curb as a dump. That's why we have rules and regulations."...

A recent two-year study by the Quebec Health and Safety Research Institute found that two-thirds of that province's garbage collectors spend time off work each year because of injuries. It discovered that in an average hour, a worker makes 482 flexes, 203 throws, 159 twists, and 53 jumps off a moving truck. These calisthenics, often done in busy streets, are performed in all extremes of climate and with minimal protective equipment.

Homeowner negligence also claims its share of collectors, the chief culprits being those who put out bottles, overloaded containers, oozing caustic liquids and exploding aerosol cans.

Yet, riding the back step of a rearpacker this day, Mike Hearty is content. It is a glorious fall morning, he is earning more than $17 an hour, and the work has been relatively light. Heavy seasons for garbagemen are April to June and mid-September to late November, when people are doing spring and fall cleanups. "The first warm weekend of spring, they go crazy," he says, "throwing out the set of barbells they've had in the garage for 40 years."

Mr. Hearty, 46, is dressed in what, if he were 20 years younger and 60 pounds slimmer, would be the height of grunge (layers of large, untucked shirts and jackets, half-laced boots and a ball cap). He has been "in garbage" for six years, the first three as a part-timer, and along the way suffered a back injury that laid him up for three months.

He arrived in Etobicoke as an unemployed shipper seeking "anything. I got garbage. It's pulsing through my veins now. I like it, as much as you can enjoy pitching garbage. You are outdoors, you've got company and you're pretty much your own boss. It can be pretty miserable in the rain, though."

He lists his job qualifications as "strong arms, strong back, weak mind."

Mr. Hearty, a "spare" with no set route, is teamed today with Barry McAllister, 32. In seven years, Mr. McAllister has been off work for two weeks due to injuries, and this morning he would gash his leg on a broken bottle protruding from a green garbage bag. In garbage, unknowns are the hazard. "If you know what you are handling, it's no problem," he tells me, a one-day visitor on the route. "A lot of people hide stuff: paint, oil, broken glass. They put it in the bag and figure you'll never find it again. We find it! Same with overweight containers. You feel that twinge when you grab a heavy can and next morning you can't get out of bed."

On a fine morning, if they didn't move so quickly—"the quicker you get it done, the happier everyone is"—pitching trash is not such a bad experience. You quickly get used to the smell and the interesting purées of crabapples, dog crap and rotten potatoes extruded by the compactor plates.

If you're sensible about lifting with your legs and not over-rotating your spine, you find the main muscle strains come in your fingers and feet. Grab and lift a 30-pound [13 kg] garbage bag a couple of thousand times and at day's end you won't be playing *Moonlight Sonata* at the keyboard. You also realize it is just as easy to walk between the 1000 or so calls as to continually jump up and down off the truck's high backstep.

One develops an individual style. Mike Hearty has perfected the behind-the-back toss. Barry McAllister is a master at scooping garbage bags while squatting on the rear curbside step of a moving truck. I'm adept at falling over cans because I have too much momentum when I jump off.

Metal garbage cans are another menace. They dent and they tear flesh with their hundred rusty edges. Plastic containers don't rust or provide natural leakage vents so the garbage stays sloppy and, in the winter, frozen to the sides. A new generation of oversize bins on wheels enable householders to roll awesome loads to the curb, mindless of the poor slob who has to lift the bins over the tailgate.

"Some people think garbage cans are furniture!" says Mr. Hearty. "I don't deliberately damage cans, but ya gotta bang 'em to get the garbage out." After initial trepidation about how to handle other people's property, I feel a complacency set in. Flip lids off with gloved hands (ear plugs, safety goggles, helmets and reflective vests are issued but seldom used). Grab the can or bag and, bending the knees, swing up a metre over the tailgate. Dump. Bang the can to rid it of clinging residue and swing it back to the boulevard. As long as it makes the boulevard and not the road or the sidewalk, don't be too bothered if it's not upright or the lid is not on.

"Garbage picking" is frowned upon by garbagemen. "If people throw it out I figure it's *garbage*," says Mr. Hearty with mild disdain, watching a perfectly good floor lamp being flattened by the compactor.

Upscale neighbourhoods have no better quality of garbage but there is generally less of it per household (families are smaller and there is rarely more than one family per house). Work among the affluent can be more tiring because the lots are larger and the walking is longer. Richer homes also undergo more renovations, and back-breaking reno-rubble increasingly ends up at curbside, in contravention of bylaws, put there by householders wanting to save on contractor haulage fees. And why is it that inhabitants of $500 000 homes put out their garbage in the flimsiest of bargain-basement trash bags that split if you so much as look at them?

Calls that entail handling heavy, loose material in open-topped boxes are nightmares. Low stoops, poor grip, sharp edges and heavy lifts.

Faced with illegal loads, Mr. Hearty and Mr. McAllister are reasonable men. "We try to help people out," Mr. McAllister says. "We tell 'em we'll take so much. But it I can't lift it, it stays. Some will complain; some have the attitude, 'I'm the taxpayer!' But it is not household waste and they are trying to save money on our backs!"

In the event of a curbside conflict, a call is made to a supervisor. "Any beefs, I call in. I'm not paid to argue," says Mr. Hearty. "'Yes, sir! No, sir!' I agree. 'Call City Hall.' They get really mad when you don't argue."

Supervisors, all of whom are ex-garbagemen, must be doorstep diplomats. A household's garbage is rarely "missed;" much more likely is that it wasn't put out in time. Householders commonly insist this isn't so, or that collectors "don't like me." Usually the supervisor will accept a resident's word and take the garbage away in his own van or recall the truck at the end of its route.

To chronic offenders, the supervisor politely explains the city bylaws. Over time, if people don't comply or don't care and garbage begins to pile up, he will mail a copy of the bylaws and an order to comply within 72 hours. If no action is taken, the city can send a special clean-up crew and bill through taxes for the manpower, equipment and dumping charges.

For every jerk jettisoning illegal trash, many more will be pleasant, wave, say hello. While it is expressly forbidden, some will offer a small gratuity for taking away a not-quite-according-to Hoyle heap of rubbish. This is not expected, but it is appreciated.

The two workers on a rear-packer are a team. By informal agreement, they spell each other off, driving/pitching at half-hour intervals. At particularly heavy calls, the driver will back the truck up to the trash at an angle to make the pitching easier, then get out and help.

Garbagemen are not exclusively men. Etobicoke has had women part-timers; none has applied for full-time. There are no barriers except the work itself. "It is a strenuous job," says Mr. Hearty, "not something every woman could do. They are at a disadvantage because they don't have the upper-body strength." Of the women collectors he has seen, he has no complaints: "They pulled their weight."

For all the physical strains of the job, its degree of mental stress is not inconsiderable. Hanging off the side of a truck, the loader must be alert for poles, signs, branches, dogs, car doors that suddenly open and impatient motorists trying to squeeze by. And he does his job in public, where every taxpayer is a watchdog.

"Resting" at the wheel of a truck is even more stressful. The driver must manoeuvre a cumbersome vehicle through narrow sidestreets and watch traffic (garbage trucks move at a stop-and-go pace which provokes the frustration of impatient traffic around them). Most stressfully, the driver must be vigilant about children, for whom a garbage truck, with its many blind spots, has an almost magnetic attraction. "I watch my man and I watch for kids all the time. They're carefree, not careless," says Mr. McAllister.

Twice this day, Mike Hearty, Barry McAllister and I travel the 20 minutes to the "Disco Dump" (Metro Toronto Transfer Station on Disco Road). The garbage, 8320 kilograms of solid household waste, is off-loaded into a grim, concrete, four-storey, drive-in silo. It is bulldozed through chutes in the floor to transport trucks waiting to drive it to the Keele Valley landfill site.

Hopefully this newspaper [in which this article originally appeared] will be put out for recycling, but if it should end up as solid household waste, please see that it is properly bundled or contained, and is not the one-quarter pound that pushes the load over 50 pounds. You now know better.

The Baker

BY

LORNA

CROZIER

In the silence of snow
far from the city lights,
a baker is baking bread
under the stars.

He wears a long white smock,
his hat tall as a loaf
that rose too high.
There is flour
on his face and hands,
flour in his mouth and eyes.

You can't see him
              for all that white
even if you walk past the houses
into the snowy dark,
into the smells of your childhood.

But he is baking,
pounding and shaping the dough.
On every loaf he pinches a name
with his fingers, his broad thumbs.
It could be your father's name,
your mother's. You never say it
out loud, never feel it
in your mouth. Nothing
is more silent than that name.

While you sleep in your ordinary bed,
under the stars on a snowy plain
a baker is baking bread. Rows of loaves
shaped by his hands are rising.
rising for someone's funeral feast,
rising for that moment when you break
the bread, its good smell
all around you.

Out of
Sight of
Land

~

BY

**JOAN
SKOGAN**

Morning

The Polish fishing ship *Jan Łaski,* 122 days at sea, is trawling for hake in the early morning fog off Canada's west coast. *Jan Łaski's* captain, who is sixty years old and thinks he has forgotten the village where he was born because it disappeared during the war, has been peering into the radar screen's black rubber viewing hood for an hour.

The radar shows a moving point farther out to sea. According to Tofino Traffic, this is the bulk carrier *Suruga Maru,* bound for Yokohama at eighteen knots, no course change. The captain switches the radar range and a point is now displayed on his port side, closer this time. He clicks his teeth in irritation and orders the helmsman to increase speed, then turn five degrees to starboard. At home in Gdynia, his wife corrects the teeth-clicking habit, but no-one mentions it here, and he believes he doesn't make this sound when he is on the ship.

In the radio room, the transmitter spits out soft static. "Gdynia, Gdynia, Gdynia," the radio officer recites, "*Jan Łaski,* Sierra Bravo

Juliet November." He glances at the clock set seven hours ahead to Polish time, then resumes his effort to reach the Gdynia radio operator so the captain can call his wife at home. The radio officer swallows as he pauses to allow a reply from Poland, tasting the memory of cherry-jam-filled *paczek* from the stall on the square in Bydgoszcz. He moves the handset away from his mouth, closing his eyes so he can remember how the river water in the Vistula-Noteć Channel smells young and green and faintly sour....

Below decks in the factory, a thick stream of hake flows towards the man who sorts the fish onto conveyor belts feeding the filleting machines. The man looks over his shoulder out the porthole close to the water line and sees that the fog has lifted a little, leaving a band of grey sea visible. After a moment, he cannot recall what he has just seen. He turns and looks out of the porthole again.

Next to the sorter on the line, *Jan Łaski's* Canadian fishery observer, a woman, is throwing hake into a basket. She has already lost count twice because she is also watching for pollock in the piles of fish moving past her. As well, she is thinking about starting her letters later today. The letters she writes on the ship are full of detail and contrast: sunrise set alongside a glassful of coffee grounds; the crucifix in the crew's mess room mixed with the moonshine wine the fishermen make from blackcurrant juice; the bo's'n's jokes and the tragic face of the youngest motorman. Fishing areas 5-1a, 5-1b, and 5-2, which contain both La Pérouse Bank's peaks and shadows forty fathoms below the surface, and the Carmanah Point line, 241 degrees true, shooting seaward to deep water. The captain in a rage, or steadfast, or drunk. She thinks the woman in the letters from sea is easier to take—braver, brighter—than the muted, shore-side version of herself.

She counts 150 hake into three baskets so she can test the conversion rate for the Baader 182 filleting machine, then decides to describe the conversion test comedy in her first letter: how she trots along beside the conveyor belt before the test can begin, searching for hake still caught on the production line; how she signals to the sorter to dump her 150 fish onto the belt while she squeezes herself around the heading machine, past the barrier shielding the man working with the filleting blades, to watch the limp, white fillets fall onto the moving grid that carries them through the washer before they drop down to the packing table. How some fillets stick in the machinery, arriving late and ragged at the table, causing the factory foreman to argue that these frayed pieces are not "normal" production. How the men packing the tray sometimes mix the test fillets with other fish, and how she shrieks with rage or laughter when this happens.

She will say in the letter that the men in the factory are good to her most of the time. They are not forced to endure, and at last encompass her, as are the fishermen she works with for hours each day on the trawl deck. The factory workers are patient with her sampling and sorting and counting, pleased, she supposes, with anything other than the sameness of their work.

In the engine room below the crew's quarters, the youngest motorman is using a clean rag to wipe sweat from his face before he drinks water that will taste of the tin cup. He plans to double-check the boiler gauges immediately, not because there is any trouble, but to keep himself from thinking. It is fourteen days since *Jan Łaski* off-loaded her cargo of frozen fish to the mother ship in American waters. The fishing ship, in return, took on board: parts for the auxiliary engine; thousands of cardboard cartons for packing frozen hake blocks (two-thirds of these are for other Polish ships on the grounds); several tons of food—meat, potatoes, rice, cabbage, and cooking oil—as well as items purchased by the crew—vodka, beer, cigarettes, and chocolate—and the mail. For the motorman, there was a letter from his mother, who prays the Pacific Ocean will not rise up in fury to take him from her.

The motorman thinks it will not be a Pacific storm that pushes him out of the engine room's straight-edged security into the slippery green salt water. He wonders if he invented the girl he thought he married at the Church of Our Lady in Gdańsk, ten days before this voyage began. He has received no letters from her to prove she exists....

The chief engineer, mindful of the boy lost overboard in these waters from *Jan Łaski's* sister ship last season, one of the helmsmen, he thinks it was, is keeping an eye on his youngest motorman. At the same time, he is reviewing bridge hands in preparation for tonight's game.

Afternoon

The bo's'n is the only fisherman on the trawl deck. The net is out, its thick wires disappear down the ramp into the water, tracked by the churning, white line of the ship's wake. The fog has thinned over a low, grey swell. The last haul, just after dinner at noon, was only five tons of hake mixed with tough-skinned dogfish and a few yellowtail rockfish, pushing the factory into production for less than two hours.

The bo's'n looks into the drying room where boots are set in careful pairs with blue-checked shirts and padded jackets lining the exhaust pipes above them. In the cabin he shares with the second bo's'n, their belongings, from nail clippers to their wives' photographs, are arranged separately in the desk drawers, on the shelves of the one tin locker, and on the hooks fastened to the bulkheads. It is understood that this precise division of goods is necessary to demonstrate that a man may not assume he knows his neighbour entirely, even when he lives and works within a hand's reach of him.

The bo's'n reaches up to touch a smaller jacket hanging on the pipe. The woman. *Jan Łaski* has to carry a Canadian observer in these waters, of course, but why would a woman come to sea with fishermen? It is not natural. But here she is, jammed in with them on the starboard side bench, waiting to haul; running in a shuffle down the slippery, tilted deck as they do; standing at the stern as the huge codend crawls up the ramp; pitching stinking dogfish hake over the side; wading through mountains of soft hake. She takes their help with her fish basket and her broken weigh scales and her dull knives. When they work through the night, she gives them her white face and her weariness, which are the same as their own. On the ship, she becomes part of the fishermen, and because of this, she is divided from all other women. Unnatural. The bo's'n brushes hake scales from her jacket sleeves, then turns out the pockets so they will dry faster.

He hears a small, repeated sound over the mutter of the main engines, and steps back onto the deck. She is kneeling in the covered area, amidships, taking hake from a basket, measuring them against a marked board, then tossing them into another basket. A tightly bound black scarf hides her hair, broadens her face and hardens its features, obliterating the woman the bo's'n knows. He is suddenly furious, wishing he could shake this strange, fierce female creature until she softens and remembers she is only a woman. She looks up at him, unsmiling, until he walks away.

Evening

Jan Laski moves along a line of pinnacles 400 fathoms below her keel, the trawl net trailing at mid-water depth. The captain is in his cabin, performing the rituals that will enable him to bear his weariness beyond his closed door, up the ladder to the bridge; the splash of cold water, four sips of whisky, the bunk remade.

The radio officer is still in the radio room, although there are no tasks for him to perform there. He is listening to transmissions from the Polish ships working in the Bering Sea, twelve days north. The voices on these ships are complaining to one another about their upcoming crew change in Seward, Alaska, a port too small to permit anyone to avoid the sight of other crew members, or even to shop successfully. The radio officer already knows what Seward looks like, and he has no friends on Bering Sea ships this season, yet he continues to listen to the weary men far to the north, who now begin to repeat their mild complaints.

The man who sorts the fish and the others from the factory crew are sleeping. The passageways leading to their dark cabins are lined with the green hills and narrow Polish streets of their dreams.

The woman is sitting on her bunk in the dark, listening to the sea rush past below the porthole. *Morze.* The sea. A neuter noun. *Statek.* The ship. A masculine noun. *Jan Łaski,* 1455 to 1531. Scholar, diplomat. Crown chancellor of Poland. Journeyed by sea to the Holy Land and the Arab countries in 1500. Thereafter worked to ensure Poland would always have her Baltic ports. She wonders if Jan Laski came to love the ship that carried him to the Holy Land and what the sailors thought of him.

In a while, she puts on the light and takes a white, blue-rimmed water pitcher from its lashing on the shelf underneath the porthole. She fills the pitcher from the trickle of warm water at the sink and begins to wash her hair, sorting through its wind-snarled knots as quickly as the fishermen on deck untangle the trawl web, filling the white jug again and again until the water pouring over her head runs clear.

The motorman sits in the chief engineer's cabin, watching him play bridge with the doctor, the *technolog*, and the factory foreman. Now and then, he looks into the darkness behind the wandering Jew plant which trails across the engineer's closed porthole, satisfied that the talk and laughter of the card players have submerged the sound of the sea. The motorman has already spooned black tea into five glasses, set out the sugar, and sliced a lemon. He waits now for the water to boil.

The bo's'n is alone on the fishermen's bench behind the winch, splicing polypropylene lines.

Night

Close to midnight, the ship is quiet. The fog has dissolved on a rising southeast wind. The radio officer has gone to his cabin at last. The bridge players and the motorman sleep deeply while *Jan Łaski* sways on a wider swell. The bo's'n gently closes his cabin door.

On the bridge, the captain stands by a window open to the blowing darkness. He has given orders for the first officer to set the trawl again when he comes on watch at midnight. The wind will shift the hake schools, and the dawn haul may be worthwhile. The woman is watching the sea gather force from a chair bolted down beside the centre window overlooking the bow. The captain murmurs her name when he says good night and goes below.

When the captain lies down in his bunk, for an instant he sees a boy in a bed beside a window on a summer night fifty years ago, in a village across the world. Stars shine through the soft dark, a breeze flows over the rye fields, the earth seems to roll gently towards him, carrying him into sleep.

Jan Łaski is riding heavy seas when the woman leaves the bridge. The boat deck doors are latched against the waves, the passageways and stairwells are empty. There is only the ship climbing hills of dark water, pouring herself down ocean slopes and climbing again. Standing on the soaked trawl deck, the woman feels the flow of her breath lengthen to follow the repeated, gathering rush and fall of the sea, and wonders if it is the same for *Jan Łaski's* sailors and fishermen, asleep behind their closed cabin doors.

Before she gets into her bunk, she discovers the bo's'n has kept his month-old promise and made her a cord of foursquare knots. He has lashed a length of precisely ridged knotwork to the grommets on her duffel bag, making a handle so well fastened, so like the bag's bleached white canvas in colour, that it might always have been there.

Pilot

~

BY

WILLIAM

KLEBECK

t is a dull cloudy April morning, and the forecast is rain. I'm out in the stubble field waiting for Lee the cropduster to make his pass. Nearby, my young son boots around hardened clumps of dirt turned up by the cultivator last fall. He's excited by the prospect of seeing the plane.

The rest of my family—my wife and daughter, my sister and her husband—are huddled back by the quonset, out of the chill wind. Hands in her jacket pockets, my mother is standing further back, conversing with the minister.

Lee's Pawnee aircraft appears over the western horizon, a dark moving speck, at first, above the distant tree-line. The whine of the spray-plane's engine builds as he approaches. My family walk out to join my son and me in the field.

Soaring past overhead, Lee salutes us from the cockpit. He makes a wide banking turn way out east over Paulson's summer-fallow and comes in low towards us, so low it seems the front wheels of the Pawnee should kick up gravel on the grid road at our field's edge.

The side window of the cockpit is slid back, and Lee's holding, in his right hand, outside the plane, a plastic bag. A thin sprinkle of grey-white dust trails out of the bag as the plane skims over the field past us, then, when Lee's a couple hundred yards away, before he can empty it, the bag blows out of his hand and drops, still weighted, to the ground.

Let us pray, says the minister. I watch the nose of the Pawnee aircraft lift up, the plane speed away skyward, before I bow my head. I did not shed any tears when my father died last November, not at the memorial service, not afterwards.

The minister offers us some chosen, reassuring words. Lee makes one more fly past, tipping his wings. We all wave at him. He's going to drive back to join us for lunch. I tell everyone I'll meet them at the farmhouse in a little while.

As I walk across the dry furrowed land, my breathing becomes quick, deeply drawn. I pick up the plastic bag that contains the remains of my father. In a few minutes I will broadcast the rest of his ashes over our field, as he asked, but now I stand there, under the heavy sky, tears wetting my grown-man cheeks.

Before dawn today, back and forth: my way, my line fixed by the long light of the tractor's high beams piercing the morning dark. Floodlights, mounted on the top of the cab, illuminate the red frame cultivator sunk into, pulled through, ripping up the ground behind. Back and forth, yesterday's bad news repeated every half hour on the radio, I work the land. Outside the cab, the darkness thins, lifts. The large sky, lit by the rising sun, overwhelms the near horizon. At the edge of the field, in our yardsite, the steel quonset gleams.

Broad daylight, I drive straight into this pothole. Drawn down by the heavier load, the tractor's engine labours. Behind me, the tandem wheels of the deep tillage push up balls of mud. The moist ground draws forty-two broad steel shovels down deeper into it. My drive wheels, losing traction, begin to spin.

I can hear you. The best way to get out of a pothole is not to get into one. And now I can see you, leaning back there against the driver's door of your old '73 rust-spotted yellow half-ton truck parked just off the worked part of the field. Pulled down low on your forehead, a cap with OPRYLAND stencilled on the front. Arms crossed in front of you, workboot heels shoved into the earth, you're grinning as I spin my wheels, shaking your head.

You get a guy out here who's a couple years out of high school, and he's never lost or fought for anything, and he goes by the book and tells me what to do. The assistant loans manager in the Credit Union these days is a rosy-cheeked young guy named BROCK PETERSON, if the black-and-white nameplate on his glasstop desk is correct. He sits with my file, my whole history, open in front of him, tilting back in his cushioned swivel chair, fingering the perfect knot in his paisley tie all the time I'm explaining my situation.

The Credit Union's been debiting my operating line-of-credit to make the payments on the mortgage I took out to buy that Murdoch land in '84, at $80 000 a quarter, so now I'm already up to my authorized limit. I need an extension this spring to cover some of my costs— seed and fertilizer, spray and fuel—until I can seed the rest of my grain.

He asks how much grain I have on hand, how many acres I plan on seeding this year. When I tell him he murmurs something about their land loan being undersecured. You want some more credit, Mr. Landis, he says.

Follow the breadcrumbs, boy, I want to say, but I don't I just nod my head. That's why I'm here.

My son, Calvin, older now. He's fiddling with the radio in the half-ton on our way back from town. Driving past Hurrell's land, Rudneski's land, our land, I tell him where we're driving, seventy years ago, was mostly bush, like right over there on his side of the road. Then Ukrainians, Icelanders, settlers like his grandfather came out here, got a quarter section of bush land, one hundred sixty acres of hard work. The homestead. And they sawed down trees, used teams of horses for pulling out roots and rocks. Small fields they cleared out of this land, and just look how thick that bush is.

But, as usual, Calvin's not listening. He's too busy bopping to the pop music blaring out of the radio. He's a smart kid, though, wants to go to university when he graduates high school. He wants to become an aerospace engineer. The future's out there, he says sometimes, pointing up.

It is one of those rare, perfect harvest nights in late August, cloudless but warm, windy enough to keep the dew off the wheat swaths. It's past midnight and the grain is nowhere near tough yet. We should be able to combine all night.

In the middle of the field, wearing only a short-sleeve shirt, I'm lying on my back on top of the roof of the three-ton truck. Above me, against an endless purple backdrop, stars winking beyond, fistfuls of colour are continuously opening up, extending long nimble fingers of red and green and pink across the dark sky. It's as if the northern sky is being played by a masterful, colourful pianist, and I'm so captivated by the performance I don't even notice the floodlights of the combine blinking on and off until it's almost adjacent to where I'm parked on the field.

What the heck—he shouldn't have the hopper full yet. He just unloaded the last one into the back of my truck less than ten minutes ago.

I slide down over the windshield onto the hood, then swing around the open door onto the seat behind the steering wheel. When I pull up underneath the auger of the combine, my father is standing on the platform just outside the cab, leaning against the railing. No grain is visible at the top of the hopper.

That usually means breakdown.

I wait in the truck as he clambers slowly down the ladder and opens the passenger door before stepping off the combine onto the running board of the truck. There's a wince on his face when he sits down on the bench seat. He lifts, with both hands, his stiffened right leg into the truck behind him.

I think I got to go home, son, he says. For the past few days he's been quietly complaining about pain in his back, and today, at supper, he mentioned his leg was, for some reason, starting to swell up.

I can run the combine for a while, I say, if you want to take a rest.

My father straightens his back, lifting himself off the seat. I don't think I can even drive the truck, he says, rubbing his knee.

I'll shut the combine down, I say.

After I dump the wheat in the hopper onto the truck, I idle the diesel engine for a few minutes before pulling the Stop button and cancelling all the lights. I drive the half-full three-ton truck across the field, slowing down near the yellow half-ton parked near the main road.

Just go, my father says. We can pick up my truck tomorrow.

I pull onto the main road. With my father beside me, the northern lights flashing in the sky above us, I drive the five miles north from what we call the South Half to our farm yard, not realizing that night would be the last time my father would work any of our land.

A farmer should go out of his way a considerable distance not to drive his tractor into a pothole. I can hear you.

Now you're taking off your cap, your greasy finger adding another dark smudge to the underside of the peak. You pass your other hand back over your head, pressing down the thin strands of grey hair that remain. You're still grinning, rubbing it in.

When your drive wheels begin to slip, gear down.

Geared down, my wheels are still spinning, flinging clumps of mud back behind me. I know. The tractor has power enough to propel itself and pull its load through the field, providing it has traction, providing its drive wheels don't slip.

One of the proudest days of my life starts out like most other days in late July. It's the end of the crop year and we're hauling grain, scrambling to deliver all of last year's crop to the elevator before the initial price drops again on August 1st. It's hot—it seems like it's always the hottest day of the year when we haul barley—and that morning it's windy, so windy, when we park down near the row of granaries and both open the doors at the same time, my permit book blows off the dash of the big truck.

Like all other days before he got sick, my father climbs inside the bins when they're almost empty to help me shovel the grain out of the corners. Despite his age, breathing heavily in the air thick with disturbed dust, he scoops just about as many shovelfuls of barley into the hungry auger as I do.

But after we put the last load of barley on the three-ton that afternoon, I tell him to go on up to the house. I'll take the load to town. I hop up into the driver's seat of the truck, but, before I drive off to the elevator, I watch my father, his legs slightly bowed, the back of his workshirt darkened with sweat, make his way slowly up the hill to the old house.

After making the delivery to the elevator, I take the Wheat Pool cheque, the proceeds from the sale of all my grain that day, to the Credit Union.

I remember, nine years ago, a young kid with long hair and dirty jeans, just after I proposed to Cheryl, going in there the first time to ask for a loan. I'd stood around outside on the sidewalk for a while, hesitating, before I finally took the big step and opened up the glass entrance door. I walked right up to the counter and told one of the tellers I come to see about a loan to buy some land.

She led me down the hallway and showed me the open door to the manager's office. Ed Florie was still around then, sitting behind a desk messy with lots of loose papers and thick file-folders. He was a working man's banker. His sportcoat was hung over the back of his chair and his long shirtsleeves were rolled up to the elbow. He looked up when the teller said there was a young gentlemen here wanting to discuss some business with him.

Sure, sure, he said, gesturing for me to sit down in one of his office chairs.

I told him I'd been working on the farm with my father the past three years, since leaving high school, and I was thinking about getting married. I thought it was time to strike out on my own. I told him I had a handshake deal with Big Jim Hafford to buy a good half-section of land a couple miles up the road from our farm. I hoped they could help me out.

Sounds good to me, Ed said, and started filling out my loan application right then. When he passed the form across the desk for my signature, he said, Just have your father come in, co-sign, and the funds will be ready when you need them.

Just like that, I was a farmer.

Now, when I get back out to the farm after doing my business in town, I stop by my father's two-storey house before going home to our newer three-bedroom bungalow on the other side of the yard. As soon as I step into the porch, I smell boiled cabbage; my mother's been making cabbage rolls again. I hear steaks sizzling in a frypan on the stove in the kitchen.

I take my boots off in the porch, spilling a few kernels of wheat out on the worn remnant welcome mat and walk into the living room.

With his feet up, my father's sitting in his favourite chair, the recliner that has one padded arm beaten out of shape, pounded pulpy by his right fist when he gets excited watching Saskatchewan Roughrider games on TV. He's still got his work clothes on.

I sit down on the chesterfield near him.

Dad, I say.

His grey eyes shift from the weather on TV to me.

I paid off the loan on the Hafford land. I dig in my shirt pocket for the paper I got from the Credit Union today. Here's that guarantee you signed for me.

He doesn't say anything. The lines in his face, on his high forehead, at the corners of his eyes, do not relax, nor do they become more pronounced. He just takes out of my hand the paper that bears his fading signature.

From the kitchen my mother yells, Soup's on.

You hungry, son? my father asks. I felt proud, simply asked to dinner.

When we were first married, Cheryl used to stick our unpaid bills on the fridge with small, brightly coloured magnets the shape of vegetables. Not any more.

One day this spring Ray Tamblyn drives into the yard in his bulk-fuel truck. Our family has dealt with his family for more than twenty years. Calvin and I are down by the shed, changing over to shovels from spikes on the cultivator. Tamblyn drags the hose out from underneath the truck and climbs up on the small wooden ladder leaning against the steel stand. We walk over as he fills my five-hundred-gallon galvanized tank with diesel.

Just come from Dave Hunter's, Tamblyn says, standing above us. Dave Hunter's a farmer down the road. He's a fellow who summerfallows, doesn't use much fertilizer or chemical because he believes it's bad for the land. Tamblyn says Hunter went to a lawyer yesterday who charged him three hundred bucks to tell him he should give his land to the bank.

Not much surprises me these days.

Tamblyn climbs down the ladder when the tank is full. As he folds up the heavy hose, I start to write out a cheque. Tamblyn slams shut the metal door below his truck tank, and stands up to face me.

Shell's putting the pressure on me to come up myself with the bills over ninety days, he says. He won't accept my cheque. I got to deal with you on cash basis, Emery, he calls me, in front of my son. I'm sorry.

I go up to the house to get some of the twenties Cheryl and I keep in the drawer in the night-table in our bedroom. On my way through the kitchen, my shoulder brushes against the fridge. My daughter's latest crayon colouring flutters to the linoleum floor.

Unhitched, without a load, you can sometimes pull yourself out. In neutral, idling, I open the door of the cab and hop down three steps onto the field. The dual drive wheels of the tractor are buried in mud to the hub. The heels of my cowboy boots sink inches into the moist ground when I walk around the tractor and rip out the hydraulic hoses, pull the pin on the cultivator.

Back inside the cab, wiping oil off my hands with a rag, I see you, with your cap on, getting into your half-ton truck.

I let the clutch out slowly, ease up the throttle. If the drive wheels grip gradually, gain some traction in solid ground beneath the mud, I'll get out of here on my own. But, as the engine gains power, I feel underneath me the rubber tire lugs tearing deeper into the wet earth.

I kick the clutch in, stopping all motion, and turn, in the tractor cab, in the driver's seat, toward you. But you're gone. Your departure today, in the old yellow truck, leaves no trail of dust whatsoever.

I climb down out of the stuck tractor. I know. Another power unit, another tractor, hitched in front, will probably get me out. This time, as soon as my feet hit the ground, I break into a run. Across our field, across the dark, soft, tilled land I worked once more this morning, I run for home. In our yardsite the steel quonset reflects the sun. Above the horizon a jet stream streaks the blue sky.

Bound
Upon A Wheel
of Fire

~

BY

SALLIE

TISDALE

Every winter night of my childhood, my father built a fire. Every element of the evening's fire was treated with care—with the caress of the careful man. The wood, the wood box, the grate, the coal black poker and shovel: He touched these more often than he touched me. I would hold back, watching, and when the fire was lit plant myself before it and fall into a gentle dream. No idea was too strange or remote before the fire, no fantasy of shadow and light too bizarre.

But for all the long hours I spent before his fires, for all the honey-colored vapors that rose like smoke from that hearth, these aren't the fires of memory. They aren't my father's fires. When I remember fire, I remember houses burning, scorched and flooded with flame, and mills burning, towers of fire leaping through the night to the lumber nearby like so much kindling, and cars burning, stinking and black and waiting to blow. I loved those fires with a hot horror, always daring myself to step closer, feel their heat, touch.

My father is a fireman. My submission to fire is lamentably obvious. But there is more than love here, more than jealousy—more than Electra's unwilling need. It is a fundamental lure, a seduction of my roots and not my limbs. I am propelled toward fire, and the dual draw of fascination and fear, the urge to walk into and at the same time conquer fire, is like the twin poles of the hermaphrodite. I wanted to be a fireman before, and after, I wanted to be anything else.

Firemen are big, brawny, young, and smiling creatures. They sit in the fire hall with its high ceilings and cold concrete floors and dim corners, waiting, ready. Firemen have a perfume of readiness. They wash their shiny trucks and hang the long white hoses from rods to dangle and dry. And when the alarm rings, firemen turn into hurrying bodies that know where to step and what to do, each with a place and duty, without excess motion. Firemen wear heavy coats and big black boots and hard helmets. They can part crowds. They are calescent and virile like the fire, proud, reticent, and most content when moving; firemen have their own rules, and they break glass, make messes, climb heights, and drive big loud trucks very fast.

Forgive me; I am trying to show the breadth of this fable. I wanted to be a fireman so much that it didn't occur to me for a long time that they might not let me. Fires marked me; I got too close. The hearth fire was my first and best therapist, the fire-dreams were happy dreams of destruction and ruin. The andiron was the ground, the logs our house, and each black space between the logs a window filled with helpless people, my father and mother and siblings. The fire was the world and I was outside and above, listening to their calls for rescue from the darting blaze, and sometimes I would allow them to escape and sometimes not, never stirring from my meditative pose. If I felt uncharitable, I could watch the cinders crumble from the oak and cedar like bodies falling to the ground below and the fire turn to ashes while I, the fire fighter, sat back safe and clear and cool.

At odd times—during dinner, late at night—the alarm would sound, and my father would leap up, knocking dogs and small children aside as he ran from the house. I grew up used to surprise. He was a bulky man, and his pounding steps were heavy and important in flight; I slipped aside when he passed by.

The fire department was volunteer, and every fireman something else as well. My father was a teacher. We had a private radio set in the house, and we heard alarms before the town at large did. It was part of the privilege of fire. Before the siren blew on the station two blocks away, the radio in the hallway sang its high-pitched plea. He was up and gone in seconds, a sentence chopped off in mid-word, a bite of food dropped to the plate. Squeal, halt, go: I was used to the series; it was part of our routine.

Then my mother would stop what she was doing and turn down the squeal and listen to the dispatcher on the radio. His voice, without face or name, was one of the most familiar voices in my home, crowned with static and interruptions. My mother knew my father's truck code and could follow his progress in a jumble of terse male voices, one-word questions, first names, numbers, and sometimes hasty questions and querulous shouts. She stood in the hallway with one hand on the volume and her head cocked to listen; she shushed us with a stern tension. She would not betray herself, though I knew and didn't care; in the harsh wilderness of childhood, my father's death in a fire would have been a great and terrible thing. It would have been an honor.

The town siren was broad foghorn call that rose and fell in a long ululation, like the call of a bird. We could hear it anywhere in town, everyone could, and if I was away from our house I would run to the station. (I had to race the cars and pickups of other volunteer firemen, other teachers, and the butcher, the undertaker, an editor from the local newspaper, grinding out of parking lots and driveways all over town in a hail of pebbles.) If I was quick enough and lucky enough, I could stand to one side and watch the flat doors fly up, the trucks pull out one after the other covered with clinging men, and see my father driving by. He drove a short, stout pumper, and I waved and called to him high above my head. He never noticed I was there, not once; it was as though he ceased to be my father when he became a fireman. The whistle of the siren was the whistle of another life, and he would disappear around a corner, face pursed with concentration, and be gone.

Oh, for a fire at night in the winter, the cold nocturnal sky, the pairing of flame and ice. It stripped life bare. I shared a room with my sister, a corner room on the second floor with two windows looking in their turn on the intersection a house away. The fire station was around that corner and two blocks east, a tall white block barely visible through the barren trees. Only the distant squeal of the alarm downstairs woke us, that and the thud of his feet and the slam of the back door; before we could open the curtains and windows for a gulp of frigid air, we'd hear the whine of his pickup and the crunch of its tires on the crust of snow. The night was clear and brittle and raw, and the tocsin called my father to come out. Come out, come out to play, it sang, before my mother turned the sound off. He rushed to join the hot and hurried race to flames. We knelt at the windows under the proximate, twinkling stars, in light pajamas, shivering, and following the spin of lights on each truck—red, blue, red, blue, red—flashing across houses, cars, faces. We could follow the colored spin and figure out where the fire must be and how bad and wonder out loud if he'd come back.

There were times when he didn't return till morning. I would come downstairs and find him still missing, my mother sleepy-eyed and making toast, and then he would trudge in. Ashen and weary, my father, beat, his old flannel pajamas dusted with the soot that crept through the big buckles of his turnout coat, and smelling of damp, sour smoke.

I should be a fire setter. I should be that peculiar kind of addict, hooked on stolen matches and the sudden conflagration in mother's underwear and father's shoes. There are plenty of them, many children, thieving flame and setting its anarchic soul free in unexpected places. But I lack that incendiary urge; my Electra is more subtle, the knotty recesses of my own desires cunning even to me.

"What we first learn about fire is that we must not touch it," Gaston Bachelard writes in his book *The Psychoanalysis of Fire,* in the course of explaining the "Prometheus Complex" that the prohibition against fire creates. I talk about my father infrequently, always with hunger and anger; I build fires almost every winter night. But I've never built a wrong fire, and I worry over flammables like a mother hen. I'm scared of being burned and of all of fires' searing lesions. I class it with the other primitive, deadly joys: the sea deeps and flying—the runaway edge of control.

I fear one particular fire. My father was also an electrician, a tinker of small appliances. I am wary of outlets and wires of all kinds, which seem tiny and potent and unpredictable; the occult and silent river of electrical fire racing behind the walls can keep me awake nights. Electricity is just another flame, but flame refined. (In this way it is like alcohol: literally distilled.) Not long ago I put a pot of water to boil on my stove, and a little sloshed over; suddenly a roaring arc of electricity shot from beneath the pot and curved back upon itself. The kitchen air filled with the acrid smoke of burning insulation and the crackling, sputtering sound of short circuits, and I didn't have the slightest idea what to do. I wanted my father to put it out, and he was 300 miles away. It seemed the most untenable betrayal, my stove lunging out at me in such a capricious way. It seemed *mean;* that arc of blue-white current burned down my adulthood.

Prometheus stole more than fire; he stole the *knowledge* of fire, the hard data of combustion. I wanted all my father's subtle art. I wanted the mystery of firewood and the burning, animated chain saw, the tree's long fall, the puzzle of splitting hardwood with a wedge and maul placed just so in the log's curving grain. I wanted to know the differences of quality in smoke, where to lay the ax on the steaming roof, how the kindling held up the heavy logs. What makes creosote ignite? How to know the best moment to flood a fire? What were the differences between oak and cedar, between asphalt and shake? And most of all I wanted to know how to go in to the fire, what virtue was used when he set his face and pulled the rim of his helmet down and ran inside the burning house. It was arcane, obscure, and unaccountably male, this fire business. He built his fires piece by piece, lit each with a single match, and once the match was lit I was privileged to watch, hands holding chin and elbows propped on knees, in the posture Bachelard calls essential to the "physics of reverie" delivered by fire.

I build fires now. I like the satisfying scritch-scratch of the little broom clearing ash. I find it curious that I don't build very good fires; I'm hasty and I don't want to be taught. But at last, with poorly seasoned wood and too much paper, I make the fire go, and then the force it exerts is exactly the same. That's something about fire: All fire is the same, every ribbon of flame the same thing, whatever that thing may be. There is that fundamental quality, fire as an irreducible element at large; fire is fire is fire no matter what or when or where. The burning house is just the hearth freed. And the fire-trance stays the same, too. I still sit cross-legged and dreaming, watching the hovering flies of light that float before me in a cloud, as fireflies do.

How I wanted to be a fireman when I grew up. I wanted this for a long time. To become a volunteer fireman was expected of a certain type of man—the town's steady, able-bodied men, men we could depend on. As I write this I feel such a tender pity for that little, wide-eyed girl, a free-roaming tomboy wandering a little country town and friend to all the firemen. I really did expect them to save me a place.

Every spring we had a spring parade. I had friends lucky enough to ride horses, others only lucky enough to ride bikes. But I rode the pumper and my father drove slowly, running the lights and siren at every intersection and splitting our ears with the noise. We the firemen's children perched on the hoses neatly laid in pleated rows, bathed in sunlight, tossing candy to the spectators as though, at parade's end, we wouldn't have to get down and leave the truck alone again.

He would take me to the station. I saw forbidden things, firemen's lives.

On the first floor was the garage with its row of trucks. Everything shivered with attention, ripe for work: the grunt of a pumper, the old truck, antique and polished new. And the Snorkel. When I was very small, a building burned because it was too high for the trucks to reach a fire on its roof; within a year the town bought the Snorkel, a basher of a truck, long, white, sleek, with a folded hydraulic ladder. The ladder opened and lifted like a praying mantis rising from a twig, higher and higher.

Above the garage was the real station, a single room with a golden floor and a wall of windows spilling light. The dispatcher lived there, the unmarried volunteers could bunk there if they liked; along one wall was a row of beds. No excess there, no redundancy, only a cooler of soda, a refrigerator full of beer, a shiny bar, a card table, a television. I guess I held my father's hand while he chatted with one of the men. In the corner I saw a hole, a hole in the floor, and in the center of the hole the pole plunging down; I peeked over the edge and followed the light along the length of the shining silver pole diving to the floor below.

I remember one singular Fourth of July. It was pitch dark on the fairgrounds, in a dirt field far from the exhibition buildings and the midway. Far from anything. It was the middle of nothing and nowhere out there on a moonless night, strands of dry grass tickling my legs, bare below my shorts. There was no light at all but a flashlight in one man's hand, no sound but the murmurs of the men talking to one another in the dark, moving heavy boxes with mumbles and grunts, laughing very quietly with easy laughs. My father was a silhouette among many, tall and black against a near-black sky. Then I saw a sparkle and heard the fuse whisper up its length and strained to see the shape of it, the distance. And I heard the whump of the shell exploding and the high whistle of its flight; and when it blew, its empyreal flower filled the sky. They flung one rocket after another, two and four at once, boom! flash! One shell blew too low and showered us with sparks, no one scared but smiling at the glowworms wiggling through the night as though the night were earth and we the sky and they were rising with the rain.

Only recently have I seen how much more occurred, hidden beneath the surface of his life. I presumed too much, the way all children do. It wasn't only lack of sleep that peeled my father's face bald in a fire's dousing. He hates fire. Hates burning mills; they last all night and the next day like balefires signaling a battle. He hated every falling beam that shot arrows of flame and the sheets of fire that curtain rooms. And bodies: I heard only snatches of stories, words drifting up the stairs in the middle of the night after a fire as he talked to my mother in the living room in the dark. Pieces of bodies stuck to bedsprings like steaks to a grill, and, once, the ruin of dynamite. When my mother died I asked about cremation, and he flung it away with a meaty hand and chose a solid, airtight coffin. He sees the stake in fire. He suffered the fear of going in.

I was visiting my father last year, at Christmastime. There are always fires at Christmastime, mostly trees turning to torches and chimneys flaring like Roman candles. And sure enough, the alarm sounded early in the evening, the same bright squeal from the same radio, for a flue fire. There have been a thousand flue fires in his life. (Each one is different, he tells me.)

As it happened, this time it was our neighbor's flue, across the street, on Christmas Eve, and I put shoes on the kids and we dashed across to watch the circus, so fortunately near. The trucks maneuvered their length in the narrow street, bouncing over curbs and closing in, and before the trucks stopped the men were off and running, each with a job, snicking open panels, slipping levers, turning valves. We crept inside the lines and knelt beside the big wheels of the pumper, unnoticed. The world was a bustle of men with terse voices, the red and blue lights spinning round, the snaking hose erect with pressure.

The men were hepped up, snappy with the brisk demands. And the house—the neighbor's house I'd seen so many times before had gone strange, a bud blooming fire, a ribbon of light behind a dark window. Men went in, faces down.

My father doesn't go in anymore. He's gotten too old, and the rules have changed; young men arrive, old men watch and wait. He still drives truck. He lives for it, for the history and the books, his models, the stories, meetings, card games. But he's like a rooster plucked; I have a girlish song for Daddy, but I sing it too far away for him to hear.

I wanted to feel the hot dry cheeks of fever and roast with the rest of them. I wanted to go in, and I kept on wanting to long after my father and others told me I couldn't be a fireman because I wasn't a man. I wanted to be the defender, to have the chance to do something inarguably good, pit myself against the blaze. I wanted it long after I grew up and became something else altogether, and I want it still.

"That which has been licked by fire has a different taste in the mouths of men," writes Bachelard. He means food, but when I read that I thought of men, firemen, and how men licked by fire have a different taste to me.

I live in a city now, and the fire fighters aren't volunteers. They're college graduates in Fire Science, and a few are women, smaller than the men but just as tough, women who took the steps I wouldn't—or couldn't—take. Still, I imagine big, brawny men sitting at too-small desks in little rooms lit with fluorescent lights, earnestly taking notes. They hear lectures on the chemistry of burning insulation, exponential curves of heat expansion, the codes of blueprint. They make good notes in small handwriting on lined, white paper, the pens little in their solid hands.

Too much muscle and nerve in these men and women both, these firemen; they need alarms, demands, heavy loads to carry up steep stairs. They need fires; the school desks are trembling, puny things, where they listen to men like my father, weary with the work of it, describing the secrets of going in.

That Ain't Working

BY BILL SASS

t's Monday morning and you hate your job. The air is stale and so is the cafeteria gossip. The lights in your office are so dim a mole would need a reading lamp. All day you'll be cramped in a tiny cell reading snotty memos from people who finished behind you in college. Or you'll spend eight hours typing someone else's snotty memos.

On days like this, you dream about The Ideal Job. That precious place of employment where you could finally be fulfilled.

The usual ideal jobs most of us think up when we're kids—doctors, nurses, teachers, police officers and tenured bureaucrats—seem to be disappearing faster than political promises.

So we [The Edmonton Journal] thought we'd look around town and come up with a new list of ideal jobs. But what is the ideal job? A mattress tester? An ice cream taster? How about Hollywood star? We don't seem to have any openings in Edmonton in these areas. But look we did and we found some people who think they have great jobs. All of these jobs, however, involve a paycheque and doing what you enjoy doing. In the end, that sounds like as good a definition of ideal as we're going to get.

Thumbs Up

Normally, *Journal* personnel aren't considered fair game for stories ("get off your duff and find us some REAL people!") But what the heck. All of us here are waiting for movie critic Marc Horton to roll the credits on his career so the fight for his job can start. What could be better than watching movies for a living, for Pete's sake?

"Nothing," says Horton. "It's a great job."

But it's more than watching movies. It's watching 400 of them a year; the good, the bad, the kick boxing.

"I can't pick and choose like the normal moviegoer."

Indeed, he sits through the block-busters and the skull-busters alike.

"As a moviegoer, I'd never pick *3 Ninjas Kick Back*. I don't look down on people that like kick-boxing movies, but I always wonder why they just don't pick up a gun and shoot someone."

That aside, "I never get tired of it. I think if William Shakespeare were alive today he'd be making movies. He was a genius who communicated with everyone."

Horton says he's wanted to be a movie reviewer since he saw his first movie at age seven in the theatre next to his house in Yellowknife. It was *My Pal Trigger,* starring Gabby Hayes.

He got his current post by apprenticing at more mundane reporting jobs like cop reporting, city reporting, sports writing and editing. He's been putting stars on movies since 1986.

"I never want to do anything else," he says.

Darn.

Perks. He thinks of them as business trips to L.A. where he has to interview the likes of Jodie Foster and Martin Scorsese. Foster, he adds, is "a great actress, but a bad interview."

He has passes to movie theatres. The paper pays for his videos.

He gets his name in movie ads in the *New York Times.*

"I don't eat popcorn."

Downside? Well, he actually has to write about the movies he sees.

The salary for this ideal job? "They pay me well." The reporter salary range runs up to and over $56 000.

Send in the Clown

Getting paid to make people feel better—what could be more ideal?

Psychologists do it, but it takes a long time, costs lots of money and they don't get to wear funny clothes, neat make-up and pull rabbits from hats.

Jojo, *nee* Joy Langley, has been clowning around for 13 years. Before that, she had a country band. When her voice went slightly raspy she detoured a budding musical career in Hamilton, Ont. into a small business in Alberta as a maker of balloon bouquets.

One day a woman wanted a bouquet delivered to a bingo hall by a clown. The rest is history. "It's very fulfilling and I wouldn't trade it," says Jojo/Joy. "I make people forget what they're worried about. I step into Jojo and that's who I am."

Did all this—the character, the magic, face painting and balloon tricks—come naturally?

"After nine kids you have to be a clown anyway," she chuckles.

She has passed on the profession to two of her sons. But behind all the greasepaint and loud clothes is a job. "It's a serious job. If people are unhappy when I get there I have to make them happy before I leave or I haven't done my job."

And what does the job pay? Jojo gets $90 for a birthday party, $250-$350 for an office party and $65 an hour to paint faces. "It definitely keeps the wolf away."

I Think, Therefore...

How about a job where all your best work happens inside your head? Fred Van de Pitte is a professor of philosophy at the University of Alberta. He gets paid to think. "We're supposedly putting all the pieces together."

A lot of workers feel—and sometimes succumb—to job and life tensions. Philosophers, says Van de Pitte, ideally avoid such things because they can put everything into perspective. "The main thing is to be thoughtful about human existence. If you have some sense of priority in how you go about being a human being, then you might be a good philosopher."

Van de Pitte figures his role is to get other people thinking along with him. "If you are literally excited about something, the teaching comes naturally."

But what good is thinking? "What we do might not have a particular application—but we help people sort things out."

Philosophy teaches there is more than one way to solve a problem—and that people with opposing viewpoints aren't necessarily wrong. "Two people can disagree completely, and neither might be wrong."

Van de Pitte got into the thinking business almost inadvertently. "I got out of high school and was drafted into the U.S. Army during the Korean War. I don't know what happened, but when I got out, I knew I would go into university and go into philosophy."

He hesitates over a word and decides to use it anyway. "You just decide you're interested in pursuing wisdom."

No one has ever lost by investing in thinking, he said. "People who invest in pure research have faith in humanity. I'd rather put my trust in people than oil."

What you can make thinking: $40 000–$80 000-plus at the university level.

Don't Make Waves

There he is: tanned, muscles rippling in the sun, surrounded by swim-suit-clad, adoring females. The lifeguard.

Yep. Collin Opper, a lifeguard for 12 years, likes his job as a guard at Mill Creek Pool. But sometimes the image gets to him. He doesn't deny the part about lifeguard groupies. "Sometimes that is the case, there's a fun part to it, but there's a very serious part as well."

Take the job title, for instance: Life guard. That pretty well says it all and Opper and all the rest of the lifeguards in the city's indoor and outdoor pools are highly trained to do just that.

They've got all those Royal Lifesaving courses under their belts— from hauling your sorry carcass out of the water to getting your personal machinery going again. Some have taken pool management. All of them have a pretty good chance of saving your life and keeping your injuries to a minimum. They have to requalify and upgrade on a regular basis.

Is it an ideal job? Well, ideally a lot of lifeguards might like to use their higher education degrees for the purposes for which they were intended (Opper has a business diploma). But lifeguarding will do. "Pool people are fun people."

Salary: $12.15/hr.–$16.07/hr.

Puttering Around

Ted Prebushewski works up to 14 hours a day, six days a week. He loves every minute of it. He's a golf pro and spends his working life doing what many duffers actually have to steal minutes to do—hang around a golf course. Prebushewski is a pro at Gold West Golf Club. He's an executive without an ulcer.

"The people in golf are so friendly. They all have a great attitude when they come here." Sometimes their attitude has cooled by the time they add up their score—but there's always the next time.

He spent 20 years on the amateur circuit in B.C., Alberta and Saskatchewan before taking the pro plunge. "I wanted to test my game." So, two years ago he took the Canadian Professional Golfers Association test and qualified for a "B" rating. For that you have to shoot 158 in two rounds on a CPGA approved course. An "A" rating calls for a 152.

He dispenses lessons, advice and golf equipment. He actually golfs two or three times a week. "Which is plenty." In winter, he heads to San Diego and takes a busman's holiday, playing golf wherever he finds a course.

But even pros have their dreams. "Eventually you want to run your own course."

On golf: The toughest part of the job is to keep your composure and focus.

On advice: Get lessons. Learn how to do it right.

On money: An assistant pro makes $10 000–$15 000 in salary. With lessons, they might make $35 000 a year.

A head pro gets $28 000–$120 000, depending on lessons and club.

Only the Lonely
Here's a job for the ultimate introvert. The ads portray a skilled loner, collecting a salary for feeding a cat and waiting for the phone to ring. Alas. All trained up and no place to go. "I'm so lonely," moans Maytag tech Al Bouffard, playing up to the image.

Bouffard has been a Maytag repairman for 12 years. He works for Maytag Home Appliance Centre. Actually, Bouffard does have a busy schedule—but points out that most of the repair work he does is more the result of customer negligence than of the machines themselves. "They neglect the exhaust or don't scrape their dishes before putting them into the dishwasher."

But while he does actually work for a living, Bouffard thinks being a Maytag repairman is a fairly neat job. He likes the job and the product. "It's not something I thought of."

He started out at the bottom, delivering machines and showing customers how to use them. Then he started fixing them—and found it challenging work.

He'll live with the advertising-induced image. Nothing succeeds like success. "But it wouldn't be a day if I didn't hear about it from somebody."

Salary: "It's a living. I'm satisfied."

Fashionable Fun

Glamor, clothes, world travel, international attention—a face to launch a thousand lucrative contracts. All parts of the modelling business. Not to mention free haircuts.

"I thought it would be easy—but it's not," says Holly Masse, a freshman model, 10 months down the road to fame and fortune.

She got interested in the profession at age 15 when her cousin took a modelling course. When she moved to Edmonton from Edson she took a course of her own, put together a portfolio and found an agency.

"It's fun. It's enjoyable and the people are very nice."

Essentially, Masse is self-employed, but...and there's always a but, "there's lots of little things that are bad." For instance, she's on a career-long diet and exercise program to make sure her measurements fit the range currently in demand. The industry is now moving out of one of its "Twiggy" phases and into a phase where women models who look like, well...women, are more in demand.

"I can't get my hair cut without permission from the agency," she said. Nor can she dye it. Again, it's a matter of getting work—sometimes a struggle for a new model when any work, from showing off shoes or new hairdos in Edmonton, becomes as important as a stroll down a runway in New York or Paris.

But there they are, the fashion capitals of the world. The model's ideal. "I hope to go overseas. I've had a couple of chances to go, but it didn't work out."

Masse will keep trying and keep putting up with the standing, smiling, sore feet and stress because if she makes it, she makes it big. Junior models make $45 an hour, to start. They have to find their own hours. Super models can make $10 000 a day. At that point, the hours find you.

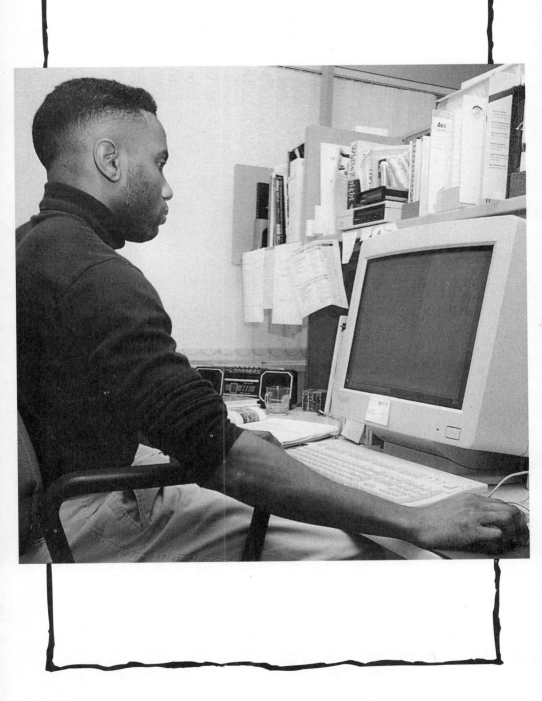

The Painter

~

BY

ROBERT D.

HOEFT

"What color?" he asks
and offers a smorgasbord of choice.
His clothes, after years of labor,
represent a rainbow anthology:
baby's pink from nursery,
colonial grey, russet,
somber/cheerful residue
from newlywed first homes
to retirement caves
where the dwellers sit
staring at/not seeing his work.
Dap-dap, dap-dap, the brush
slushes over scars of time,
over sun fade, over years
of rain and wind sniping,
over death, suicide, birth,
fresh beginnings, departure.

He deals in choices,
fresh appearances,
new starts.
He moves up his ladder
changing reality
one rung at a time.

Debbie Tewa— Building a Future With Her Community

BY

WINONA LADUKE

t's a sun-baked mesa in northwestern Arizona. Debbie Tewa's strapped on her toolbelt and hardhat. She clambers up a ladder onto the flat roof of a 200-year-old stone house. She looks out over a hundred miles of desert, and takes a deep breath. She glances across the village, sees the sun glinting off the roof-based panels, and smiles. She is home, and she is the Hopi Foundation's solar electrician.

Since 1991, this community-based Native foundation—*"Lomasumi-nangwtukwsiwmani,"* in their language, has placed photovoltaic solar panels atop 50 houses on the reservation. All of them were installed by this woman—a thirty-two-year-old Coyote Clan resident of Hotevilla. This project, like others of the Hopi Foundation, is embracing both the past and the future.

It makes sense. One third of Hopi's villages have refused to accept electrical power lines into their village areas. The Hopi object to the electricity on several grounds. Village leaders are concerned about preserving their sovereignty as village entities. They see their people becoming "hooked" on public utility power, only to be compromised when the people are unable to afford the ever-increasing monthly payments. "They don't allow powerlines into the villages, because the utilities will also have the right of way," Debbie explains. Village leaders "think that if we don't pay up the bills, they'll take even more land. So, when you get your own system, it's yours, there's no powerline, no right of way into the villages, so we have our own land."

Other arguments against the power are spiritual and cultural. The Hopi Foundation explains that "the force field of electricity emanating from the powerlines is considered to be disruptive to the atmosphere, ambience, and balance of the plaza and ceremonial areas, at the same time blocking the aesthetics of the sky and the panoramic vistas of the mesas."

The Long Road

And so, each day before climbing onto the rooftops, Debbie begins with a cup of coffee at the office, lining up her schedule, and her equipment. Debbie came into this job down a long road. Raised by her grandmother, on the Hotevilla plaza, Debbie moved later to nearby Tuba City with her mother till the eighth grade. She graduated valedictorian from the BIA boarding school in Riverside, California, and returned to Arizona to go to school at Northern Arizona University in Flagstaff. "I wasn't doing too well in school so I quit," she laughs. "Then, I went selling Avon for a while, till I got this job, as the coordinator for the summer youth at Hopi in 1983."

Debbie started thinking about trade schools when a recruiter for the Hopi tribe began interviewing her summer youth students. "I asked her if girls could apply, and she said 'yes,' so in 1983, I got accepted to go to a trade school," where she ended up in Electricity. "I went to school for a nine-month course, and then I got a job with the Gila River Housing Authority, changing devices in the HUD homes."

So began a string of jobs with various electrical companies in the Tempe area. She got contracts, showed some real talent, and then more and more jobs. "Eventually, I ended up with this company called Delta Diversified and I worked with them for about three years. I started out as an electrical helper, and then eventually was promoted to a foreman. I stayed there about a year, and then I quit, because they were building a PHS hospital at Gila River, and they paid more money. It was a federal job. So, I stayed there for a couple of months, and then eventually got laid off, and was more or less on my own for a while and got odd jobs. I wired houses for people, here and there, had a contract with the Home Improvement Program, and then the Hopi Foundation got hold of me. That was in late 1989."

Debbie ended up in a solar energy training program in Carbondale, Colorado. When she returned, the Hopi Foundation had started their program, part time in 1989, and then slowly speeded up. In 1991 she began fulltime work at the foundation, which now employs three people—a manager, a secretary, and an electrician—Debbie.

The Hopi Foundation, at its core, represents a way of dealing with the physical, social, economic, and spiritual consequences of change in communities. The Hopi believe that there is a strength in the preservation and revitalization of culture and self-determination. The Hopi Foundation recognizes that members of their community have increasingly demonstrated their desires for modern conveniences, which are powered by electricity—a reasonable expectation for those living in the 20th century, but the foundation believes there are ways to do that without destroying a way of life, or an ecosystem. That solution, in Hopi land, is solar energy. But, that is energy which is, frankly, put in with a conscience, not just with a powerline.

Debbie talks about the change in perspective brought around by solar energy. "We're so accustomed to the conveniences of having the electricity, having some guy come over and hook you up to have power. With this system, you purchase it, and it's yours. It teaches you to be conservative, because you're getting your power from the battery, you can't just leave your hallway light on for three or four hours. It teaches you to be independent."

Solar energy and the Hopi Foundation also changed Debbie's life. She gets to work in her own community. "I really enjoy working at home. Just the interaction with the customers, the people—I get to talk my language, that's nice. I get to learn a lot up here, especially with the older folks. When you're out there in Phoenix, you talk to people, you get fired, or get these looks. Here you get to talk to people. I don't mind hauling water, or getting through the mud to get to work. Sure beats driving in the big city traffic to get to work. I don't miss that one bit. We don't just do photo voltaics, I do trouble-shooting, I can add on, or if they're hooked up to the old grid, I can help them with that.

Women's Work

How does Debbie's work influence other young women in the village? There is first the question of what traditional jobs are for Native women in this day and age. "I asked the question, I wonder what people will say about this. I thought whatever happens, happens. This could show the high school kids that you could do whatever you want to do, whatever job you want, go for it.

"Now I have some respect from the kids, too. They say hi to

me, and ask me questions about being an electrician, and stuff." She feels support from the community, for the most part. "There's maybe people who talk about me, but that's fine. But for the most part, I get a lot of encouragement, especially from the old people, and that's really a good boost. They say something like this in Hopi: "You're taking care of yourself. It doesn't matter how you do it, but it's your own thing. Nobody's giving you the money to do this and that. It's your own thing."

There are some other young women who may be following in her footsteps. "Now, there was one girl, who was thinking of going into carpentry, and there was another girl who wanted to get into electrical work in Hotevilla. So that's a start."

For other Indian communities, Debbie also has, when asked, a few words. "A long time ago, the Native Americans were all ecologists, and if you really think about it, solar energy conserves, and it fits into that environmental scheme. Because you don't use the electricity from generating plants, you aren't damaging the environment. I think it's something that each community should look at. They can look into other things. Or solar hot water heating, you can heat up the water through the sun, with these panels on your roof—the water goes up to the roof, and then comes down hot."

Women, according to Debbie, also can have a big impact in this area, if they think about these issues, and the numbers. Debbie explains, "Women usually take care of the household, and they have jobs. They can look into solar energy, and they can educate themselves about the environment. I educated myself about the environment and this can help a lot. The women in the house are paying the bills. They can invest in some of these products and that can save them a lot of money, and that can improve the efficiency of their house. They could get into this field, and get jobs for themselves in this field, or help their community themselves."

As for herself, Debbie lives in a one-room house with an outhouse. "My kitchen, bedroom, living room are one room, and they're hooked up solar." She invented a solar shower (since there's no plumbing in her house) and she's thinking about a composting toilet. She's definitely on the cutting edge of Hotevilla, but that edge is something which appears to be carefully crafted. We may all be able to learn something from her, and this community.

Sweetheart

BY

MOLLY

MARTIN

I was doing pretty good on this new job. See, they didn't want to hire me. Said four foot eleven was too short to be a mechanic. The trucks are put up to a certain height they said and I wasn't tall enough to reach them. But after I complained to Fair Employment, they decided it was okay for me to use a ladder.

So here I am on my little ladder under a diesel changing the oil. The roll-up doors on the garage are all open so I'm kind of on display. And I'm the first woman so I'm a curiosity. They all make detours past the maintenance shop just to see me on my ladder. As if I was a two-headed snake or something. Strange how their minds work. Or they'll come in with some "problem" just to get a look at me. Sometimes they'll walk past and make comments, sort of muttered under their breath, but I know they mean for me to hear. I try not to, though. I concentrate on my work and try to ignore them. They're chicken, any-how. I say, you don't like somebody, you just tell 'em to their face. I'd have more respect for them if they talked right to me.

One time I thought I heard the word "bitch" but when I turned around the guy was gone, out the door. Now I don't know if it really happened or if I was just paranoid. I decided it doesn't really matter one way or the other, whether I hear it or not. They're trying to get my goat. They're letting me know they don't want me. Well, you do that to me, it's like waving red in front of a bull. No way am I quitting now. The more they bug me, the harder I dig my heels in. Besides, this is the best money I ever made. Beats waitressing any day.

So anyhow, I'm standing there under this truck and I hear from across the yard kinda sing-song but loud, "Hey sweetheart, how ya doin' today?" I squint out into the sun and see this big old red-faced guy waving his arms at me. His belly looks like a hundred pound sack of flour slung over a farmer's shoulder. His waving arms cause the sack of flour to jiggle and expose a rim of pink flesh above his belt. His head looks like an engine block, hair shaved into a military flat top. He must be a teamster, I think. No neck.

I gotta admit my first impulse was to laugh at this fool. Next I wanted to punch his lights out. Now I know some women don't mind being called sweetheart or honey or any of those sugar-coated names. Men will tell you women think it's a compliment—especially older women. Then they look at me as if I should understand. You know, I'm not that old, but it seems like I hate this name calling more the older I get.

I decided if I ignored this joker maybe he'd get the point and leave me alone. Wouldn't you know, that tactic only encouraged him. Every time he'd see me, he'd yell "Heeeeey sweeeetheart" at the top of his lungs so everyone could hear. One day he came right up and introduced himself, friendly as can be. "Hey," he says, holding out a grimy hand, "I'm Harry. Harry the Hunk they call me." I'm like, is he kidding? Harry the Hunk! Is he putting himself down? I had to hide a smile. I wanted to appear serious, intimidating if possible.

"My name's Bev," I scowled, "and I'd appreciate it if you'd call me that."

"Okay, sweetheart," he leered, and walked away.

Well you can imagine, that got my dander up. I fumed about that all week. It got so every night I'd be beating up Harry the Hunk in my dreams. Now I've never been one to criticize any woman for how she chooses to survive in a job. We each pick our own battles. God knows you can't take on every one that comes along. You'd be wrung out like a dishrag at the end of every day. Some insults are better ignored, but some if they were water wouldn't even slide off a duck's back. So I determined to take on Harry the Hunk or my mind would never be set at ease as long as I worked on this job.

By this time I've been on the job a while and I've gotten to know the crew of mechanics in my shop. They turned out to be a pretty good group after all. Dave struck me as a Hell's Angel type at first glance. Kinda scruffy, his beard half grown out. Yeah, I know that's in style now, but believe me on him it looked scruffy. Skinny as a cotter pin and at least six three. Drives a Harley. He's the first to talk to me. "Don't let 'em get to you," he says. "I know what you're going through. My wife's a sheet metal apprentice."

I'm like, no kidding. We were instant friends.

Well, that broke the ice. The others might have been a little jealous of Dave, or they might have decided I'm no more different from any of them than they are from each other. Two are immigrants, from Ireland and El Salvador. The rest are blacks, whites, and Chicanos.

We circled around each other for a while, testing limits. I had to tell one or two not to call me girl or honey. Had to thank them for their offers of help, but let them know I've got two arms, I can carry things just like taller people. Maybe better, 'cause I'm closer to the ground.

I did almost get into a scrape with the foreman, Fernando, a very proper gentleman who let me know in so many words he thinks women belong at home and not in a garage earning a man's wage. In his world women don't leave their children to go to work, they don't wear pants, and they don't swear.

Now all my friends know I can cuss a streak as blue as any long-shoreman. I let the guys know swearing doesn't bother me at all. So I'm starting to feel real comfortable in the shop, and one day I'm shooting the breeze with Fernando trying to tell him I deserve a good job, I've got three kids to support just like him when I guess I let a four-letter word drop. Well, he gets this look on his face all kind of fur-rowed and scrunched. I swear the corners of his mouth drooped more than his mustache. His eyes turned into little black ball bearings under his bushy brows. Then he draws himself up and says, "Dear, I don't see any reason to use that word."

'Course I know this is not true, since I hear the guys say it all the time. What he means is he has a different standard for women and men. Well, you know I'll fight for a lot of things, but my right to swear at work is not first on my list. So I say, "Okay, Fernando, I'll make a deal with you. I'll never swear in front of you again, if from now on you call me Bev instead of dear." He thinks this is an honorable agree-ment, and we even shake on it, though I suspect he doesn't think women ought to shake either.

Turns out Fernando took me seriously. Called me by my name from then on. I've kept my part too, ever since, and our truce stood me in good stead in my ongoing battle with Harry the Hunk. Fernando could see what was going on. So, after that, when Harry would come through the shop, before he could even get his big mouth open, Fernando would yell at him, "Heeeey sweeetheart."

This should have been enough to make any grown man blush, but Harry just took it in stride. He'd smile sheepishly and go about his business. But he wouldn't stop calling me sweetheart.

Then one day I hear Harry lay the same trip on Dave. "Hey, hippie," he says, "when are you gonna get a haircut?" Harry's smiling the whole time, but I can tell Dave doesn't think its funny. Dave just keeps his mouth shut and concentrates on his brake job.

Harry keeps smiling at me, too, and I start to figure out the only way he knows how to be friendly is harassing people. But I decide I don't care, I never liked being called names and I'm not gonna get used to it. If he wants to make friends he's got to at least learn my name.

One day I put it to him. "Harry," I say, "why do you keep calling me sweetheart when you know I hate it?"

"You hate it?" he says. "But I call my wife sweetheart and she loves it."

"Harry, I'm not your wife, I'm your coworker, Bev. I'm not your sweetheart." Now I'm thinking this guy is thick. He really doesn't get it. This is gonna be harder than I thought.

A while later he brings in his truck for emergency work and I'm the only mechanic available. "Come on," he says, "hop to it, sweetheart. I gotta get this baby back on the road."

"Harry," I say, "either you never learned the mechanics' law or you forgot it."

"Mechanics' law, what's that?" he says.

"Very basic," I say. "The law says you treat your mechanic right, you got a smooth running truck. Treat your mechanic bad and your truck never gets out of the shop. Harry, if you don't stop calling me sweetheart, you could be a permanent pedestrian."

"Okay, okay," he says, "if it means that much to you. I really need my truck…Bev."

I could see his mouth had great difficulty forming the word, but it was a start. After that, he seemed to try harder. He'd bolt into the shop in his usual back slapping, shoulder punching way and yell, "Hey, Swee…Bev." This was a great improvement, and I told myself I'd made progress, but Harry seemed to be having a hard time making the transition. I couldn't tell whether his harassment had taken a new form or his mind just wasn't making the connection.

Now that we're "friends" Harry thinks he can take new liberties. One day he lopes over, yells, "Hey Swee…Bev," and wraps his arms around me in a bear hug. I duck, but not soon enough, and he gets me in a headlock.

I growl at him, "Harry, what are you doing?"

He looks hurt. "Just saying hello."

So after that whenever he sees me he holds his arms outstretched as if to hug me and gets this sad teddy bear lost puppy look on his face. God, I think, I've created a monster.

"Jeez, Harry, go hug an I-beam."

Harry finally learns to say my name without having to stop and think every time. Natural as can be, he comes in and says, "Hey, Bev, how ya doin'?" We chitchat about our kids, I ask him how his wife puts up with him. He tells me she's really a liberated woman. I start to actually like the guy, but as soon as I let him know that, he thinks all the rules are off. He thinks he can call me whatever he wants and I'll go along with the program.

I run into him as I'm hurrying across the yard on my way back from lunch break. "Hey, sweetheart," he grins, arms outstretched as he walks toward me. I can see if I keep walking I'll head right into his grasp, so I have to stop and move sideways like a crab to avoid him.

When this happens, I frown, cross my arms, look him straight in the eye and say something like, "Harry, go drive your truck off a cliff." I'm trying to let him know I'm not playing, but to him this is the game.

One day he walks into the shop with a woman. I should say amazon. This woman's gotta be six feet tall. Built like a linebacker. Her skin is the color of Colombian coffee. Her black hair is knotted up under a red kerchief and she's dressed in work clothes and boots, so she's got to be working here. Another woman in the yard! I'm thinking, who is she, what does she do, when Harry brings her right over to introduce me.

"Sweetheart," he booms, "I want you to meet my new partner, Pam." He's grinning so wide, his teeth take up half his face.

Now people say I'm easygoing. I'm known for my high boiling

point. But I swear when Harry says this I feel like an engine overheating. Smoke must be coming out of my ears. I have to hold my arms next to my sides to keep from strangling him, and I start yelling all the words I promised Fernando I wouldn't.

"Aww, come on," he whines, "I was only kidding."

"Harry," I hiss, "don't call me sweetheart. It's not funny, it was never funny, and it's never gonna be funny."

When he turns around and walks out of the shop I hope I never see the jerk again. I also hope Pam doesn't think I'm a total nut case. I do want to talk to her. But a little while later Harry slinks back in, alone this time, and stands beyond punching distance from me, head hanging, and says in a low voice, "Bev, I'm really sorry. You know I didn't mean to make you mad. I was just showing off to my new partner. I promise, I'll never do it again."

"Right," I say, and jerk my socket wrench so hard I take a slice of skin off my thumb knuckle when it hits the block.

By this time I don't trust Harry the Hunk for a minute, and I tell myself I'm never gonna get set up again. So I just try to avoid him and be real busy whenever he comes by. He still acts friendly and says hi and I try to be civil. He always calls me Bev, still yelling as loud as ever. And because I'm not a person who can hold a grudge, I loosen up and let my defenses down some. Pretty soon we're back to our old routine. But he's never called me sweetheart since.

One day he stops by and gives me a hand with a generator I'm trying to move. "Thanks," I say. "I don't care what they say about you. You're okay."

"Hey, Bev," he grins, "all that work paid off. I turned out okay, huh."

"Yeah, Harry," I say, "and it only took me five years."

Think Like a Weightlifter, Think Like a Woman

BY KATE BRAID

First day on the job and the foreman orders
in a voice like a chainsaw,
Hoist those timbers
by hand to the second floor.
Crane's broken down.

I keep my mouth shut
with difficulty, knowing
how much a six-by-six timber
twelve feet long and fresh
from the Fraser River, knowing
how much it weighs.

Lorne, my partner, says nothing,
addresses the modest mountain of timbers
towering over our heads, smelling
sweetly nostalgic for forest.

Weighing in with the wood he faces,
with a belly like a great swelling bole,
he shakes off my motion to help and
bends as if to pick up a penny,
scoops up the timber and packs it, 50 feet,
to lean against the damp grey sides
of the concrete core.
When he doesn't look back,
it's my turn.

And now, because I need this job, and
because it's the first day and because
every eye is watching The Girl,
I bend my knees as the book says,
think like a weightlifter, take the beam
by its middle and order my body
to lift.

Reluctantly, the great tree, sweating pitch,
parts with its peers with a sucking sound,
and the beam and I sway to the designated spot,
I drop it. Repeat.

Alone, I carry beams to Lorne
who alone heaves them with the slightest grunt
to the labourer who bends from the second floor
with a hurry-up call,
Faster! Faster!

*No. I will never be a carpenter, I think, never
able to work like these men.* Then
Lorne falters.
Without thinking I reach up my two arms beside him
and push with all my might.
The beam flies to the second floor and mindless,
I turn to fetch him another.

Without a word
Lorne follows me back to the pile,
lifts one end and helps me
carry the next timber to the wall.
Without a word we both push it up,
continue this path together
find a rhythm, a pace
that feels more like dancing.

Lorne says, *You walk different. Yes.*
For on this day I am suddenly
much, much stronger, a woman with the strength
of two.

Putting Value on Housework

~

**BY
KATRIN
NAGELSCHMITZ**

he question, "do you work?" is a loaded one.

It is no longer a safe way to start a party conversation—not just because of high unemployment—as more people realize employment is only one area of work. Parenting, housework and volunteering are also work. If you have small children, are responsible for dinner every day, or run bingos for a service club, you know that.

What is your answer? Do you say, "I work part-time," even though those are the hours which feel often like time off from the responsibilities of family and home? Do you say, "I don't work," even though your volunteering fills more than 40 hours a week?

Mother's Day is the time we show our respect and love for our mothers. Motherhood is more than a state of mind, though. Motherhood is work and it is high time for Statistics Canada to see it that way too.

When StatsCan asks in the census every five years, "do you work?" it only wants to know about work done to earn money. If you are a full-time parent, homemaker, and/or volunteer, you have to answer "no." Will this be changed for the next census? StatsCan is testing questions regarding housework, family care and volunteer work (it has been done before, but the information was deemed unsatisfactory).

What is also needed to make this change happen is political will. Women's organizations across the country are lobbying to have unpaid work included as "work" in the next census.

What difference does it make whether or not unpaid work is included in the census? The information which the census collects is considered a comprehensive picture of the lives of

Canadians. This is what economic and social policies are based on and these policies do affect everyone. How good can they be if they assume only paid work is relevant to Canada's standard of living?

According to a recent StatsCan study, housework performed by Canadians last year [1993] equalled 46 per cent of Canada's gross national product. (GNP is the total of the paid goods and services produced in the country). All the work done within the millions of Canadian households is not part of the picture when governments use labor statistics to develop policies—neither the care given to children, spouses, parents and neighbors, nor the time spent in the kitchen or laundry room. There are as many hours spent with unpaid work as with paid work. One-half of all work that keeps this country going is invisible in the census.

When the work is invisible, then the life of those who do the work is invisible. The message is it is not work and of no value. How can homemakers feel good about themselves when we are tired after a day of housework and child-rearing, and have not even "worked"? How can we develop and maintain self-esteem, if we put everything into doing a good job, and then hear this is not a "job"? How can we have stable relationships, if one person is considered a "dependent" of the other?

Mothers sacrifice financial independence. As long as the unpaid work is valued by those around her, the "just" means less money today—and less money in old age. If the unpaid work and responsibility she carries for the family is not valued, however, then her life can be downright dangerous, as low self-esteem and economic dependence prevent women from leaving abusive relationships.

Could Canada do without unpaid work? Housework, family care and volunteer work all provide essential services to people and communities. Without these services individuals and societies could not function. Some of it could be delegated to paid work. This has happened in recent years, as more women entered the paid work force. However, women with full-time employment still work another 35 hours each week in the home (men average 11 hours).

Not all unpaid work can be delegated—even if we could afford it. Work done for its own sake rather than for money is different—for the person who does the work, as well as for those who benefit from it.

When people do something for us, for our own sake alone, it makes us feel good about ourselves. It makes children feel good about themselves, when time is taken to listen to them or to take them along. It makes neighbors feel good, when people invest time and energy into their community. Children, families and communities who feel good about themselves can make more good things happen. This is how we all benefit from caring families and vibrant communities. They are the building blocks of a stable and prosperous society.

What is considered the economy? Today it is defined by the exchange of money. However, the literal meaning is "management of a household." The purpose of money is for the household to provide goods and services it cannot produce itself. Before the Industrial Revolution, members of a household produced within it the necessary food, clothing and shelter for its members. The strong distinction between housework and the workplace is only a recent phenomenon.

Housework, family care and volunteer work are more important than ever to our standard and quality of life. As the economy and social systems continue to change, Canada cannot afford to take mothers (and fathers and volunteers) for granted any longer.

None of This is Fair

BY

**RICHARD
RODRIGUEZ**

y plan to become a professor of English—my ambition during long years in college at Stanford, then in graduate school at Columbia and Berkeley—was complicated by feelings of embarrassment and guilt. So many times I would see other Mexican-Americans and know we were alike only in race. And yet, simply because our race was the same, I was, during the last years of my schooling, the beneficiary of their situation. Affirmative Action programs had made it all possible. The disadvantages of others permitted my promotion; the absence of many Mexican-Americans from academic life allowed my designation as a "minority student."

For me opportunities had been extravagant. There were fellowships, summer research grants, and teaching assistantships. After only two years in graduate school, I was offered teaching jobs by several colleges. Invitations to Washington conferences arrived and I had the chance to travel abroad as a "Mexican-American representative." The benefits were often, however, too gaudy to please. In three published essays, in conversations with teachers, in letters to politicians and at conferences, I worried the issue of Affirmative Action. Often I proposed contradictory opinions. Though consistent was the admission that—because of an early, excellent education—I was no longer a principal victim of racism or any other social oppression. I said that but still I continued to indicate on applications for financial aid that I was a Hispanic-American. It didn't really occur to me to say anything else, or to leave the question unanswered.

Thus I complied with and encouraged the odd bureaucratic logic of Affirmative Action. I let government officials treat the disadvantaged condition of many Mexican-Americans, with my advancement. Each fall my presence was noted by Health, Education, and Welfare department statisticians. As I pursued advanced literary studies and learned the skill of reading Spenser and Wordsworth and Empson, I would hear myself numbered among the culturally disadvantaged. Still, silent, I didn't object.

But the irony cut deep. And guilt would not be evaded by averting my glance when I confronted a face like my own in a crowd, By late 1975, nearing the completion of my graduate studies at Berkeley, I was so wary of the benefits of Affirmative Action that I feared my inevitable success as an applicant for a teaching position. The months of fall—traditionally that time of academic job-searching—passed without my applying to a single school. When one of my professors chanced to learn this in late November, he was astonished, then furious. He yelled at me: Did I think that because I was a minority student jobs would just come looking for me? What was I thinking? Did I realize that he and several other faculty members had already written letters on my behalf? Was I going to start acting like some other minority students he had known? They struggled for success and then, when it was almost within reach, grew strangely afraid and let it pass. Was that it? Was I determined to fail?

I did not respond to his questions. I didn't want to admit to him and thus to myself, the reason I delayed.

I merely agreed to write to several schools. (In my letter I wrote: "I cannot claim to represent disadvantaged Mexican-Americans. The very fact that I am in a position to apply for this job should make that clear.") After two or three days, there were telegrams and phone calls, invitations to interviews, then airplane trips. A blur of faces and the murmur of their soft questions. And, over someone's shoulder, the sight of campus buildings shadowing pictures I had seen years before when I leafed through Ivy League catalogues with great expectations. At the end of each visit, interviewers would smile and wonder if I had any questions. A few times I quietly wondered what advantage my race had given me over other applicants. But that was an impossible question for them to answer without embarrassing me. Quickly, several persons insisted that my ethnic identity had given me no more than a "foot inside the door"; at most, I had a "slight edge" over other applicants. "We just looked at your dossier with extra care and we like what we saw. There was never any question of having to alter our standards. You can be certain of that."

In the early part of January, offers arrived on stiffly elegant stationery. Most schools promised terms appropriate for any new assistant professor. A few made matters worse—and almost more tempting—by offering more; the use of university housing; an unusually large starting salary; a reduced teaching schedule. As the stack of letters mounted, my hesitation increased. I started calling department chairmen to ask for another week, then 10 more days—"more time to reach a decision"—to avoid the decision I would need to make.

At school, meantime, some students hadn't received a single job offer. One man, probably the best student in the department, did not even get a request for his dossier. He and I met outside a classroom one day and he asked about my opportunities. He seemed happy for me. Faculty members beamed. They said they had expected it. "After all, not many schools are going to pass up getting a Chicano with a Ph.D. in Renaissance literature," somebody said laughing. Friends wanted to know which of the offers I was going to accept. But I couldn't make up my mind. February came and I was running out of time and excuses. (One chairman guessed my delay was a bargaining ploy and increased his offer with each of my calls.) I had to promise a decision by the 10th; the 12th; at the very latest.

On the 18th of February, late in the afternoon, I was in the office I shared with several other teaching assistants. Another graduate student was sitting across the room at his desk. When I got up to leave, he looked over to say in an uneventful voice that he had some big news. He had finally decided to accept a position at a faraway university. It was not a job he especially wanted, he admitted. But he had to take it because there hadn't been any other offers. He felt trapped, and depressed, since his job would separate him from his young daughter.

I tried to encourage him by remarking that he was lucky at least to have found a job. So many others hadn't been able to get anything. But before I finished speaking I realized that I had said the wrong thing. And I anticipated his next question.

"What are your plans?" he wanted to know. "Is it true you've gotten an offer from Yale?"

I said that it was. "Only, I still haven't made up my mind."

He stared at me as I put on my jacket. And smiling, then unsmiling, he asked if I knew that he too had written to Yale. In his case, however, no one had bothered to acknowledge his letter with even a postcard. What did I think of that?

He gave me no time to answer.

"Damn!" he said sharply and his chair rasped the floor as he pushed himself back. Suddenly, it was to *me* that he was complaining. "It's just not right, Richard. None of this is fair. You've done some good work, but so have I. I'll bet our records are just about equal. But when we look for jobs this year, it's a different story. You get all of the breaks."

To evade his criticism, I wanted to side with him. I was about to admit the injustice of Affirmative Action. But he went on, his voice hard with accusation. "It's all very simple this year. You're a Chicano. And I am a Jew. That's the only real difference between us."

His words stung me: there was nothing he was telling me that I didn't know. I had admitted everything already. But to hear someone else say these things, and in such an accusing tone, was suddenly hard to take. In a deceptively calm voice, I responded that he had simplified the whole issue. The phrases came like bubbles to the tip of my tongue: "new blood"; "the importance of cultural diversity"; "the goal of racial integration." These were all the arguments I had proposed several years ago—and had long since abandoned. Of course the offers were unjustifiable. I knew that. All I was saying amounted to a frantic self-defense. I tried to find an end to a sentence. My voice faltered to a stop.

"Yeah, sure," he said. "I've heard all that before. Nothing you say really changes the fact that Affirmative Action is unfair. You see that, don't you? There isn't any way for me to compete with you. Once there were quotas to keep my parents out of certain schools; now there are quotas to get you in and the effect on me is the same as it was for them."

I listened to every word he spoke. Buy my mind was really on something else. I knew at that moment that I would reject all of the offers. I stood there silently surprised by what an easy conclusion it was. Having prepared for so many years to teach, having trained myself to do nothing else, I had hesitated out of practical fear. But now that it was made, the decision came with relief. I immediately knew I had made the right choice.

My colleague continued talking and I realized that he was simply right. Affirmative Action programs *are* unfair to white students. But as I listened to him assert his rights, I thought of the seriously disadvantaged. How different they were from white, middle-class students who come armed with the testimony of their grades and aptitude scores and self-confidence to complain about the unequal treatment they now receive. I listen to them. I do not want to be careless about what they say. Their rights are important to protect. But inevitably when I hear them or their lawyers, I think about the most seriously disadvantaged, not simply Mexican-Americans, but of all those who do not ever imagine themselves going to college or becoming doctors: white, black, brown. Always poor. Silent. They are not plaintiffs before the court or against the misdirection of Affirmative Action. They lack the confidence (my confidence!) to assume their right to a good education. They lack the confidence and skills a good primary and secondary education provides and which are prerequisites for informed public life. They remain silent.

The debate drones on and surrounds them in stillness. They are distant, faraway figures like the boys I have seen peering down from freeway overpasses in some other part of town.

Jorge the Church Janitor Finally Quits

BY

MARTÍN

ESPADA

No one asks
where I am from,
I must be
from the country of janitors,
I have always mopped this floor.
Honduras, you are a squatter's camp
outside the city
of their understanding.

No one can speak
my name,
I host the fiesta
of the bathroom,
stirring the toilet
like a punchbowl.
The Spanish music of my name
is lost
when the guests complain
about toilet paper.

What they say
must be true:
I am smart,
but I have a bad attitude.

No one knows
that I quit tonight,
maybe the mop
will push on without me,
sniffing along the floor
like a crazy squid
with stringy gray tentacles.
They will call it Jorge.

Room for All

~

BY

CHRISTINE

MICKLEWRIGHT

hift work. It can be a gross interference with your life or it may allow you to do things you wouldn't do otherwise. For those who must plan their lives around it, especially the rotating shifts, working can be a daily scramble to find order.

This is the week I struggle in early. Up at 3:30 a.m. A cool dark and lonesome hour. Out on the road by 4:30 a.m., speeding on empty roads, cursing red lights and praying for green.

Sliding my car into the parking lot. Zipping my security card into some electronic slot that winks green and releases the door for my entry. Barely on time, but here's no one to notice.

The long room is crowded with green glowing VDTs. The chairs are, for now, empty. Soon voices will clatter, chatter and clash around the machines that now sit silently, or emitting the occasional beep.

Touching keys and entering the system, it greets me, demanding I read this or that. I plunge on, printing flight schedules, checking arrivals and departures. Talking to voice recording machines telling the callers of planes coming and going. Sometimes I hear them roar overhead, see their wheels poised for touchdown, gliding in, climbing out.

Then suddenly I am no longer alone. Other shapes slip in, sign in, talking, laughing, or drifting in glazed silence. My co-worker begins his day with a gentle sigh. A relief agent, his schedule is always haphazard. Today he is happy, he has a day shift, but the rest of the week is all wrong, all evenings. This must not be and he begins the begging, pleading, bartering process with fellow workers in the great shift exchange game.

"I guess you want to be home with your family in the evening?" I inquire gently.

"Yes," he responds with a happy smile. "But more than that, I must go to the Mosque each evening."

"The Mosque—every day?" my lapsed Catholic existence injects a tone of astonishment into my voice. Once a week on Sundays was bad enough for me.

"Yes," he informs me, solemnly. "It gives me peace. It's only a short visit for maybe an hour, but it soothes my soul and gives me the inner tranquility that I need."

Images and memories tumble through my mind. Purple dawns ruptured by wailing calls for prayer broadcast by tinny speakers that have long since replaced men in minarets. Silent black shapes swirl along dusty sidewalks, the women in purdah, eyes watching from behind a crocheted lace grill, hidden from the lustful glances of men. The discomfort of a western woman standing revealed, prey to passing hands.

And I have to ask him: what of Salman Rushdie, his death sentence?

He smiles and shakes his head. "I follow Aga Khan. Our beliefs are more moderate, more modern, especially," he grins at me, "where women are concerned. As for Khomeini and Rushdie, no, this matter I do not agree with. It solves nothing."

The supervisor hovers around. Some problem is discussed and resolved, then a pause as a fellow worker interrupts with a phone message for me from some civil servant in immigration. And my supervisor is suddenly ablaze with a barely suppressed rage.

"Immigrants! It's time it was all stopped. They're abusing the system, arriving here without documents pretending to be refugees. The scams they get away with. Look at those Sikhs coming in on that boat in Nova Scotia, lying about where they came from, just to get in. All those Asians coming in every day and legitimate people wait years or can't get in at all."

I am at first stunned at this newly-exposed aspect of this little fellow. Then I am angry and there is an uncomfortable debate. "It's not like that at all," I say, trying to explain the myths and confusion about refugees and immigrants and the contributions they make to our country. My words are wasted.

My friend sits silently, staring at his computer. I realize I know little about him other than I think he could be from India, because of his accent, yet I am not sure. I know he visits relatives in Bombay, so I begin to explore his world and I am surprised.

I learn about the boyhood of this man, growing up in Nairobi. His father died when he was three and his mother raised the family alone. He mourns for the childhood he never had. Each morning up at 4 a.m. and out on the streets selling samosas (pyramid-shaped, deep-fried curried potatoes) before school and then again at the end of the day. All to make a little bit of money to help the family. His family origins are somewhat murky, perhaps Iran, perhaps India and it was several generations earlier.

"Some days," he recalls, "there was no food at all." Clothing was scarce and living was hard. He compares it now to the life of his children, a fourteen-year-old daughter and an eight-year-old son, all comfortable in this Canadian lifestyle. It is his wife who is from Bombay, the relatives are in-laws. India is not his country although the life of the poor there parallels his own upbringing on another continent.

I feel it and taste it. How many early mornings did I tramp the crowded streets of India, through five adventurous months nearly twenty years ago? Sidewalks of blanketed bodies, huddled for warmth, all their possessions clutched tightly beside them. In my hungry search for breakfast, there would always be some grubby street corner where a young boy plied his wares. "Samosas Memsahib," he would cry out, thrusting them into my hands. And I would ache for him, for this child who could not play, who must work for his family to live.

And I stare at the back of my retreating supervisor and feel the anger. The rage against those who have it all and would keep it from those in need. These people live on phoney fears, terror of takeover, of some unnamed loss, those selfish white supremacists that would keep this country sparse for themselves.

On the long plane trips to Ottawa each month, trekking my way east for a meeting about employment and immigration, I am always struck by the vastness of the land, uninhabited, sparsely populated areas contrasted with crushing, crowded, lively cities. I know there's room for all and room for more.

My co-worker turns from a conversation with another worker. He's grinning again. "This is a good week," he declares, "God is looking after me, all my night shifts are gone. Now I have day shifts. I can go to the Mosque every night. My family will be so happy."

I share his elation, even if I cannot begin to imagine such religious commitment. Just for a moment I flash back to a seat on a grubby steam train hissing in an Indian railway station. "Trains may either make up or lose time" says the sign. I am tempted to put that on the flight information recorder, sure would save a lot of bother whenever TimeAir (which we pretend is Canadian Airlines) has a problem with one plane and messes up the schedule for the rest of the day.

In my mind I see myself hanging out the window of the soot-covered train reaching towards the hands of a young Indian boy on the platform. Coins drop into his palm and I take two hot samosas from his small brown fingers. His gleaming white teeth beam up at me, then he turns quickly to his next customer.

I smile at my co-worker, relieved that he has left that terrible poverty behind. But I cannot calm my anger towards those who will not willingly share the wealth and opportunity of this nation.

For there is room for all of us.

Robt. Simpson Co. Mail Order Office, 1909

Greetings from the Electronic Plantation

~

BY

ROGER SWARDSON

Out in the economic sector where you work all week but can't make a living, lots of us are fastened like barnacles to the bottom of the computer revolution. Soldering tiny leads on circuit boards. Plugging data into terminals. All sorts of things that tend to share one characteristic: repetition. Some of the jobs, like mine, consist of sitting in a chair while, all day long, people call you from all over the country to buy things

like T-shirts that read "Compost Happens."

Just after 9 a.m., a tireless recorded voice in my headset tips me off. A catalog shopper is coming my way from across the continent. I press the appropriate key and say, "Good morning, welcome to Wireless. My name is Roger. How can I help you?"

Wireless is one of five direct-mail catalogs operated by Rivertown Trading Company, a shirttail relation of Minnesota Public Radio, the spawning ground of Garrison Keillor.

This morning I walk through a new industrial park to the cluster of smokers hanging around the lone door in the block-long wall of a warehouse. Once inside I show my picture ID to the guard behind the glass window and stick another plastic card in the time clock.

I initial the sheet that tells me when to take my morning and afternoon 15-minute breaks and half-hour lunch period. I nod good morning to two women at the group leader station that overlooks the room. They smile and nod back. Both are concentrating on computer terminals that identify scores of telephone service representatives (TSRs) like me who have logged onto the system this morning. The screens tell the group leaders exactly what all the TSRs are doing in the system and for how many seconds they have been doing it. In a seven-day period prior to Christmas 1991, despite the lousy economy, about 300 of us in two shifts wrote 87 642 mail or credit card orders, up 47 percent from the year before.

One supervisor in a headset has a distant look on her face. She's monitoring a TSR, tapping into a customer call to check on two dozen points that must be covered. The TSR will be told the results later in the day.

I fill up my coffee mug and check the printout taped to the wall next to the time card rack. The printout summarizes the results of our weekly monitorings. Ideally we should get 24 pieces of information from the customer (like home phone, work address, whether or not they want to be on our mailing list) during the course of the conversation. During the monitorings, we are graded according to how much of the data we have gotten, which is a difficult task when you've got a customer on the other end of the line who just wants to make a purchase and hang up without being asked a bunch of questions. We are expected to maintain an average above 90 percent. The names of all TSRs in the 90s have been highlighted with a blue marker. I'm at 89.6 percent. It has been suggested that I could use additional training.

I head down a double row of 20 stalls where the backsides of seated people stick out like the rumps of Guernsey cows. The room is done in tones of gray, and merchandise is pinned to white walls. The 80 stalls I can see are mostly occupied. There is a continuous yammer like audience noise before a concert. On two walls electronic scoreboards flash the number of calls completed for each of five catalogs. The total is around 2200. A busy morning. Must have been a big catalog mailing.

I find an open stall, adjust the chair height, get my headset on, and log onto the phone and computer systems, using my password. An orange light on my console indicates that there are callers on hold.

I bring up the initial screen of the order process and tap the button on my phone to signal that I'm ready to take a customer call. A recorded voice instantly says "Wireless."

I swing right into it. "Good morning. Welcome to Wireless. My name is Roger. How can I help you?"

A woman from New Jersey is distressed.

"You have to help me."

"Sure, what's the problem?"

"I ordered a ring for my husband for our anniversary. Last night we went out and I gave it to him before dinner. Well, he's put on a little weight and it didn't fit. The poor man was so upset he couldn't eat his dinner. Today he's out there running around the neighborhood and getting red in the face."

"That's terrible. What can I do?"

"Well, I looked at the ring this morning and I ordered a size too small."

"Send it back. We'll send you another one right away."

"How long will it take?"

"If you want to pay extra I can send it overnight air. Regular delivery is 10 working days."

"Make it the 10-day. It won't kill him."

"Interface" is a word that tells millions of American workers where we fit. We are devices between you and a computer system. Various terms further identify the device: data entry, customer service, word processing, telemarketing, and others. We take reservations. We do market research. We sell people aluminum siding the minute they sit down to dinner. Every night we update computer records so that multinational corporations can begin the day on top of things. We type most of today's business communications. We do all those mundane tasks that provide computer systems with the raw data that makes them useful.

Even so, most of us are among the more than 14 million Americans who work every week but are still classified by the government as poor. The people Ross Perot talks about when he says, "I suppose when they are up to six bucks an hour in Mexico and down to six bucks here, American corporations will again begin creating jobs in this country."

Here's another way we are classified. The first sentence of my employee handbook tells me that the company "believes in the practice of employment at will, which means that employment is terminable by either the employee or the company at any time, for any reason." We are devices that accommodate the economic needs of our era. Flexible. Disposable.

Even recyclable.

Say a company is "downsizing" or "delayering" or whatever other term describes job cuts. Through a combination of early retirement, attrition, and layoffs they manage to take 200 current semiskilled employees off the payroll over the course of a year. Say those employees were paid an average of $12 an hour with full benefits. The company then hires a temporary agency to fill openings as they occur. The agency may even have an office in the company's building. Job qualifications are determined, and the agency finds the people and trains them if necessary. The jobs will pay from $5 to $7 an hour. Even with the agency's commission, the company has just saved around $2 million annually in wages and benefits.

Improbable? A want ad placed by a temporary employment agency in my St. Paul newspaper lists four major corporations that need temporary workers. The agency is offering a $25 bonus to people with prior experience with any of the listed companies. Today, through the wonders of current economic policy, it is possible to replace yourself at a bargain rate.

Here's another way the system works. You have a data entry barn where the job routine is easy and repetitive. The problem is that your volume is changeable, with big bulges around some of the holidays. A permanent work force would be awkward, so you have a standing order with three temporary agencies.

When your temporaries show up, they are told their hours will vary as necessary with one week's advance notice. The temps will rarely get a full week's work. They can be sent home any time during the day or let go permanently for any reason. They will receive no benefits. They are subject to a probationary period and can be dropped with a call to the agency. In a relatively short time you have a high-performance, completely flexible work force. You can even offer the best of them permanent part-time jobs, again with no benefits but with a raise in pay. (This actually amounts to a savings, since you no longer have to pay the agency commission.)

Look at the costs and problems you have eliminated. Look how easy the system is to manage. All you have to do is keep weeding.

This is the employment system of the 1990s, made possible by a bankrupt economy and an increasingly desperate work force.

We are the vocational descendants of the dapper clerks in the better stores who knew your sizes and decided when your son ought to be ready for his first suit. Our voices, regardless of how we happen to look or feel that day, are fresh and animated and friendly. We just happen to be sitting here in jeans and a sweatshirt talking into a little foam ball.

After a while you get into a rhythm. You learn to judge how the calls will go. Women in California invariably say they have shopped with us before when they have not, men everywhere say they have no idea whether they've shopped with us before though many of them are repeaters.

Southern women sign off with "Ba-Ba" except for Texans, who just say "Ba," and people from Alaska sound like friends you can rely on, which seems fortunate in that kind of country. I never heard a shrill voice from Alaska.

You can easily tell people who are ordering with a purpose and people who love to shop or do it to feel better. One day a woman browsed through the catalog for 18 minutes and ordered more than 3000 bucks' worth of stuff. I had a pretty good idea the order wouldn't go through, but she had a wonderful time.

This two-week pay period I'm able to get in 74 hours at $6 an hour. My take-home, after federal and state taxes and Social Security, is $355.48. With another good pay period plus the 5 percent commission I make by selling merchandise on the specials list, I could net $800 this month.

On this particular day I take 57 calls from 23 states. I write $4096.59 in orders. The biggest is from a guy in California for a selection of videotapes that includes complete sets of the British television shows *Reilly, Ace of Spies* and *Rumpole of the Bailey.*

In just over eight months, working at a pace where I am either available for or taking orders more than 90 percent of the time I am logged on, I have taken 4462 orders and booked nearly $300 000.

Even so, many jobs like mine, especially in urban America, are at risk. Workers in American cities cost more than elsewhere simply because it costs more to live here. As a result, there is a kind of ongoing economic cleansing. Software "upgrades" constantly eliminate some jobs, data barns move to cheaper rural locations, and the Caribbean and Mexico are claiming jobs.

In the meantime, take that $6-an-hour job that provides about $800 a month if you can get 40 hours a week in, and then add up rent, utilities, phone, food, and transportation. Then try adding a family.

It doesn't add up.

"Recovery" is a wishful term. It is also a word that means something understandable. Most of us can tell whether we are recovering. Thirty-eight million people below the poverty line is not a persuasive definition of an economic "recovery."

Leading economic indicators are used by economists to describe conditions as they may be six to nine months in the future. How, if the present constantly worsens, can the future remain perpetually bright? Even schoolchildren can see that that's denial.

How else could "downsizing" be heralded for improving corporate profits and aiding the "recovery"? Fewer livelihoods mean "recovery"? For whom?

The same with "diminished expectations" or lesser livelihoods. That must mean those economic refugees from companies that let $12-an-hour people go and replaced them with $6 temporaries. These resettled workers are a non-statistical phenomenon. They are employed. But because millions of dollars have been hacked out of their paychecks, they no longer qualify for mortgages, car loans, or credit cards no matter what the interest rate. Who will spend us into the "recovery"?

Workers are getting pushed farther down the economic ladder as laid-off skilled workers and recent college graduates secure even the menial jobs. And, on the bottom, public assistance is breaking its seams.

Surely, the term "recovery" has become a mockery of the way millions of Americans now live.

The rest of us come and go. The young. Men without jobs. People picking up some extra money. But women between 40 and 60 are always there, plugging away at countless uninspiring jobs that need doing day in and day out, year in and year out.

On break they sit together eating homemade food out of Tupperware while the rest of us use the vending machines. They show each other craft handiwork. They bring packets of photos. They take work seriously and talk about the merchandise and what kind of a day they're having. They do well at jobs many make fun of or would not do. And they succeed at life as it is.

I left a temp job at an insurance company at dusk. A woman was sitting at a terminal in word processing wearing a smock. I said something sprightly like "Working late, huh?" And that started a conversation. It happens easily with night-shift people.

Her husband put in 27 years on the production line of a company that went broke and then cheated him out of his pension.

She worked for a small office-equipment firm and the same thing happened. He is now a part-time security guard. She holds down two temporary jobs. Their jobs don't provide health insurance, and they can't afford it. They put in a lifetime working, raising their kids, and they must continue working indefinitely. I was enraged but she passed it off. Gave me a brownie. Then in the lighted corner of the darkened office she went to work, producing letters from dictation. As I left I could hear the tape of some dayside junior exec talking through his nose about yet another intolerable situation that had come to his attention.

The caller's voice does not hold together well. I can tell he is quite old and not well. He is calling from Maryland.

"I want four boxes of the Nut Goodies," he rasps at me after giving me his credit card information in a faltering hurry.

"There are 24 bars in each box," I say in case he doesn't know the magnitude of his order. Nut Goodies are made here in St. Paul and consist of a patty of maple cream covered with milk chocolate and peanuts. Sort of a Norwegian praline.

"OK, then make it five boxes but hurry this up before my nurse gets back."

He wants the order billed to a home address but sent to a nursing home.

"I've got Parkinson's," he says. "I'm 84."

"OK, sir. I think I've got it all. They're on the way." I put a rush on it.

"Right. Bye," he says, and in the pause when he is concentrating God knows how much energy on getting the receiver back in its cradle, I hear a long, dry chuckle.

One hundred and twenty Nut Goodies.

Way to go, buddy.

During our time together I am not sucking cough drops and scratching for rent money and she, with her mellow alto, is not calling from a condo at Sea Island. We are two grandparents talking over the selection of videos for her grandson's seventh birthday. We settle on classics, among them *The Red Balloon, Old Yeller,* and *Fantasia.*

I say "we" because when I'm on the phone I identify with the people I speak with; I'm no longer an electronic menial. And it's not just me. We all do it. I can hear my neighbors. You'd think we were at a Newport garden party.

We identify with wealth because none of us, moneyless,

think of ourselves as poor. We'll be on this plantation another month. Maybe two. That $10 job will come through. That ominous feeling around the tooth will go away. The car won't break again. We'll be on our way presently.

Except there's a feeling these days that's hard to pin down. A detachment that comes out now and then as rage or despair. Many of the people I work with are bone-tired from just trying to make it week by week. A lot of people have just plain stopped believing any politician.

For years the working poor in this country have felt they had a pact with the powerful. Work hard and you'll be OK. Do your job well and you'll have the basics and a chance to move up. The rich and powerful, because they run the system, have been stewards of that promise. It means when the chips are down, the preservation of opportunity is supposed to come before the cultivation of privilege.

On the bus and in the break room today there is a great deal of frustration. The promise has been broken and people don't really know what they can do about it. Another system has taken the place of the old pact. Those who have found a secure place in the suburbs, in government, in the corporations, in wealth, have redefined the country under a different set of rules. It is a smug new club. And those riding the bus and sitting in the break room need not apply.

At the end of my shift I log off the computer and phone system, nod good-bye to the two women at the supervisory station, punch out, open my backpack for the guard so he knows I'm not stealing anything, and head for the bus.

Not a bad day. Remarkably like yesterday.

The Mind-Style of the Entrepreneur

MICHAEL
WARSHAW

*oward H. Stevenson is the Harvard Business School's point man
on entrepreneurship. Since the chair was established in 1982,
he has been Sarofim-Rock Professor of Business Administration
at Harvard University. He is also senior associate dean and director of
financial and information systems for Harvard Business School.*

*Among Stevenson's written works are four books, 41 articles, and
more than 150 cases for the Harvard Business School. He has worked
as an executive, founded his own company, and now sits on the board
of a half-dozen corporations.*

Why should anybody pursue entrepreneurship?
It offers control over your own destiny. I'm sure that the vast majority
of people would rather make their own mistakes. It's this feeling: if I
fail, at least I fail myself, rather than letting somebody else who does-
n't even know who I am determine my future.

I think it also offers more justice, or fairness. If I'm going to take
the risk, let me get the rewards.

THE MIND-STYLE OF THE ENTREPRENEUR : **157**

Why is studying entrepreneurship so important now?

In the past, people used to think a rewarding, dynamic, great career came by joining a good company, working hard, and moving up the ladder as the company grew.

When I graduated in 1965 with an MBA, I was one of 700 from Harvard, and there were only 7000 in the United States that year. This year, there are 80 000 MBAs. And now, most of the companies that my professor told me to join, so that I could work hard and have an exciting and dynamic career, don't look so exciting and dynamic and may not even be there.

In those days, the company took the risk and the employee got the reward. Now it appears that the employee takes the risk and the company gets the reward.

Think how much has changed just in technology. I have more technological capacity on my desk here than Stanford University had in its computer center as late as 15 years ago. So I can do things with my fax, with my PC, with desktop publishing, with database management software that would have required a herd of people.

In fact, if you add to that the facilities of phone systems throughout the world and the ready access to travel services, an independent entrepreneur can do things that used to require tremendous organizations.

How do you teach yourself to be an entrepreneur?

First, you have to know what it is. Scholars, like Schumpeter, defined entrepreneurship as an economic function. Today, a lot of studies focus on the personality of entrepreneurs; their drive to succeed, the early childhood experiences that gave them that drive and the ability to take risks.

Well, neither approach is sound. You can't build a single psychological profile of the entrepreneur because there are too many examples that break the rules. There are people who equate "entrepreneurship" with innovation or with founding a company. In that case, forget about Ray Kroc of McDonald's or Thomas Watson of IBM because neither was a founder. I would say, though, both were entrepreneurs.

Entrepreneurship is not an effect or a type of individual. It's a behavior. It's the pursuit of opportunity without regard to the resources you currently control.

Are you saying that anybody can learn to be an entrepreneur?

I'm saying that it's a behavior that can be understood and wielded as a tool; a tool that empowers you, whether you're a business owner, a manager, or anybody pursuing success.

I've created a model that defines that behavior between two extremes. At one end is the "promoter," who confidently pursues opportunity without worrying whether he or she has enough resources. At the other end is the "trustee," who thinks first about the resources at hand and seeks opportunity based on that inventory.

Nobody is a pure promoter or a pure trustee. But the entrepreneur leans toward the promoter end of the spectrum, consistently making decisions based on the opportunities.

What are the most important ideas to communicate when you teach entrepreneurship?

There are four basic things you do in teaching this. One, transmit some knowledge: a minimum of tax law, something about securities regulation, a few techniques of financial analysis.

Secondly, there are some skill issues that we should teach in entrepreneurship. One is presentation. I would argue that most of life is selling. Selling myself to my banker, selling my product to a customer, selling myself to my suppliers.

A third idea we work to communicate is that there are alternatives, many different solutions to a problem. In fact, there are many different forms of entrepreneurship. People must see that there are a wide, wide variety of things they can do. I have a friend who just owns 15 Taco Bells. But I think he's done pretty well.

The last thing you try to create is a set of attitudes. There are three attitudes that every entrepreneur has to have. One is that behind every situation is an opportunity for improvement. Whatever I look at, I ought to figure out a way to do it better.

A second attitude is, I have a personal responsibility for bringing that out. No matter how much I lack in resources, I'd better do something today to bring about that improvement.

And the third is an attitude that the experts and the experienced may be wrong. Many times, people with success were told by the experts and the experienced they're crazy.

At *Success* [magazine] we write about such entrepreneurs in an annual issue we call "Renegades." People who defy conventional wisdom to build their success.

It's a funny thing. Don't just say screw the experts, but if you understand why they're wrong, you must take some action.

There's an old story about the woman who cuts off the end of the roast before she cooks it. And her husband watches this for years. He asks why she does that, and she says, "Well, that's the way you cook a roast. That's the way my mother did it."

And he asks his mother-in-law why she does that. "I don't know," she says. "My mother did it that way."

He goes to see the old lady and asks, "Why did you cut off the end of the roast?"

She says, "Because I only had a very short pan." And so, much of practice evolves because Grandma had a short pan.

You seem to be making a case for entrepreneurs to do their own original thinking.

I'll give you a simple example. IBM always said wear a white shirt. A lot of people think that was a stupid rule, but if you understand why they said it, it made sense. They said, look, you will never offend anybody being dressed conservatively. Which is absolutely right. If your job is selling, what you want to do is not have them turned off by your appearance.

Being a renegade just by breaking the rules isn't good. Much more power comes from the capacity for original thinking that causes you to take creative action when other people are simply doing it the same old way.

Is that the core talent of an entrepreneur?

I think the core talent is understanding empathetically the people around them. Asking, "What do I have that they want, which I can get to them?" In many cases, it isn't money. To employees, it can be freedom, recognition, or positive feedback. For customers, it can be a little extra service.

Can you make an organization entrepreneurial?

You can restrain some bureaucratic tendencies. I think 3M does a good job. How? By allowing people to access resources fairly easily. If you have an idea, you can get a small amount of resources to pursue it.

Think of Post-its. They were invented because they made this adhesive that didn't work too well, and they forgot about it. Then one day, the 3M technician was in church and a paper fell out of his hymnal. He thought he'd like some way to mark his place without permanently marking the book. So he went back to the lab, took some of this adhesive, put it on a piece of paper, and tried it, and it worked. He started to answer memos by writing notes on these little sheets. He gave some pads of this stuff to the executives' secretaries.

Then he stopped sending them pads because he had no budget to make them. The secretaries started to complain to their bosses. And the president of 3M argued that maybe they ought to make some more. If his secretary became addicted to it, maybe some other secretaries might.

Think of what a difference it makes that he was able to get these resources. Now it's a huge business, but imagine going into a board of directors in a standard company and saying, "I found this adhesive that doesn't work well. We're going to stick it on pads of paper and charge 79 cents."

Let's see. We charge 39 cents for a real pad that is stuck together well, and 79 cents for this little thing. And we're going to create a $400-million business in 10 years. You would be laughed out of the boardroom.

Can you always defeat the competition by being more entrepreneurial than they are?

That's not all there is to it. Success and entrepreneurship are not equivalent. Many entrepreneurs are successes, but many entrepreneurs are failures. That's one of the most important things that I teach my students. I think one of the biggest impediments to entrepreneurship is the fear of failure. It restricts the pursuit of opportunity.

Done right, you can survive failure. One of my friends comes to class and talks about the day he went bankrupt. He was a supplier to the building business. He leveraged himself up very highly, and in one year, building starts in his country went from 3000 to six.

He worked his way through the bankruptcy, started another business, and is reasonably successful. More importantly, his kids are very successful.

He tells the students a story about what he calls one of life's greatest lessons. He stiffed the local gas station for $79 and was ashamed to go in. So he started to buy gas somewhere else. He was driving through the town, and the guy walked out and flagged him down and said, "Fred, I think I'm your friend, and I know you owe me money that you cannot pay, but it doesn't help me that you're buying gas from my competitor. We're friends, aren't we?"

To me, that's one of the lessons you try to teach. No success is permanent and no failure is final.

Life is a journey, not a destination. I think that's what entrepreneurship is about. It's treating the activities as a journey. It's not about the destination of being the richest person in the cemetery.

You argue for entrepreneurial behavior in every aspect of career, in every aspect of life?

Yes. Absolutely. And it is not just money. Take the case of Marvin Bower, who reformed the consulting firm McKinsey & Co. in 1939. In 1956, when Marvin owned a sizable piece of the company, the total revenues were $3 million. This year, Marvin owns zilch, but the revenues are $1.3 billion. He has made a nice amount of money and he is still the grand old man of the company.

Compare that with the Steinberg grocery chain. Sam Steinberg founded Steinberg's in Montreal and grew it so that it was eventually sold for $1.8 billion. His kids, after taxes, took home $100 million apiece. But they didn't all go to their mother's 80th birthday party.

To me, the issue is, what is an opportunity? Sam had died by this point. What would he think? The family was lost. Would he define this as success?

How did you come to this understanding?

I actually wrote the framework on the back of a symphony program one evening. I was trying to explain a couple of things that had always bothered me.

People were defining entrepreneurship as a person. Either you are or you're not. To me, most of life is a spectrum. Saying either you are or you're not avoids understanding.

So you concluded that leaning toward promoter attitudes is the most powerful means for pursuing success and avoiding pitfalls?

Yes. This is what many successful people do, whether they are business owners, artists, or professors. They look for opportunity, for something that hasn't been done.

Is it possible to lean too far over to the promoter viewpoint?

You obviously need some balance. As many big companies have amply demonstrated, you can't make widgets on Wednesday and waffles on Thursday and be successful. There's something important to knowing your territory.

Successful entrepreneurs know their business, but they don't get married to the previous concepts of the business. It's a curious challenge, because to be a successful entrepreneur, you have to know your business in detail. You have to know your customers and economics. But that doesn't mean you can be locked into those as they were.

Is it imperative to seek change?

Absolutely. Entrepreneurs have a great disrespect for the past. They create change. Whatever people think is right, they think can be better.

Is that the attitude that distinguishes an entrepreneur from somebody else?

What an entrepreneur says is, "For what opportunity do I have an unfair advantage?"

You don't want to compete in a fair game as an entrepreneur. What I want is something for which I control the edge. I want to pursue the opportunity for which I have an unfair advantage. If it's real estate, it's on a critical corner; if it's a service concept, I've got a better means of motivating and training my employees.

It's exactly the antithesis of the economists who believe in perfect markets. Do you know the story about the economist who saw a $50 bill on the ground? He wouldn't pick it up, because if it were real, somebody else would have.

I think entrepreneurs have that sort of faith. Maybe it's ego, but it's also a faith that I can perhaps recognize things that other people wouldn't see.

Murder, Inc.

BY

ROBERT

SHERRILL

here are something over fifteen hundred men and women on the
death rows of America. Given the social context in which they
operated, one might reasonably assume that they were sentenced to be executed not because they are murderers but because
they were inefficient. Using guns and knives and the usual footpad
paraphernalia, they dispatched only a few more than their own number. Had they used asbestos, mislabeled pharmaceutical drugs and
devices, defective autos, and illegally used and illegally disposed chem-
icals, they could have killed, crippled, and tortured many thousands of
people. And they could have done it without very much fuss.

Corporate criminals, as we all know, live charmed lives. Not until
1978 had a corporation even been indicted for murder (Ford Motor
Company, which was acquitted), and not until 1985 had corporate
executives ever been brought to trial for murder because of the lethal
mischief done by their company.

The executives who made history in 1985 were the president,
plant manager, and plant foreman of Film Recovery Systems
Corporation, a ratty little silver-rendering operation in Elm Grove
Village outside Chicago. The silver was recovered by cooking used X-
ray films in vats of boiling cyanide. Film Recovery hired mostly illegal

immigrants, who were afraid to protest working conditions so foul that they made employees vomit and faint. The illegals were preferred also because they couldn't read much English and would not be spooked by the written warnings on the drums of cyanide. To make doubly sure that fright wouldn't drive workers away, management had the skull-and-crossbones signs scraped off the drums. Although the antidote for cyanide poisoning is cheap and easy to obtain, Film Recovery Systems didn't keep any on hand.

So it came to pass that Stefan Golab, a sixty-one-year-old illegal immigrant from Poland, took too hefty a lungful of cyanide fumes and died. Charged with murder on the grounds that they had created such unsafe working conditions as to bring about "a strong probability of death and great bodily harm," the three officials were convicted and sentenced to twenty-five years in prison.

Will executives at other villainous corporations be similarly charged and convicted? Don't bet on it. In this instance the law was applied so properly, so rightly, so common-sensically that one would be foolish to expect such usage to appear again soon. It was a sort of Halley's Comet of Justice.

The idea of treating corporate murderers as just plain murderers strikes many people as excessive. Some lawyers who cautiously approved the conviction in principle said they were afraid it would confuse people generally because a bald murder charge is usually associated with a bullet in the gut or an ice pick in the neck, and nice people would have a hard time adapting the charge to the way things are sometimes accomplished in the front office. Speaking for this timid viewpoint, Alan Dershowitz, Harvard's celebrated criminal law specialist, said he thought the Film Recovery case showed we need a new category of crime. "We should have one that specifically reflects our condemnation of this sort of behavior," he said, "without necessarily assimilating it into the most heinous forms of murder"—as if the St. Valentine's Day massacre were any more heinous than Bhopal.

During the trial, the Illinois prosecutor accused the defendants of "callousness, disregard of human lives, and exposing people to dangerous products all for the sake of profits." No wonder the verdict has been so modestly praised. If that's enough to rate a murder charge, our whole commercial system is at risk. If it were to become the rule, we could look forward to a lineup of accused corporate executives extending out the courthouse and around the block several times.

Since there is no statute of limitations on murder, prosecutors would be obliged to charge those executives at Firestone who, a few years back, allegedly killed and injured no telling how many people by flooding the market with ten million tires they knew to be defective; and the executives at Ford who sent the Pinto into circulation knowing its gas tank was so poorly designed that a rear-end collision could turn the car into a fire trap (several dozen men, women, and children were burned alive). From the pharmaceutical fraternity would come such as Dr. William Shedden, former vice-president and chief medical officer for Eli Lilly Research Laboratories, who pleaded guilty to fifteen criminal counts relating to the marketing of Oraflex, an arthritis drug that the Food and Drug Administration says has been "possibly" linked to forty-nine deaths in the United States and several hundred abroad, not to mention the hundreds who have suffered nonfatal liver and kidney failure. Seems as how the folks at Lilly, when they sought approval from the FDA, forgot to mention that the drug was already known to have killed at least twenty-eight people in Europe. (Shedden was fined $15 000; Lilly, which earned $3.1 billion in 1984, was fined $25 000.) And let's be sure to save an early murder indictment for those three sly dogs at SmithKline Beckman Corporation who whizzed their product, Selacryn, through the FDA without mentioning that it had caused severe liver damage in some patients in France. False labels were used to peddle it in this country, where it has been linked to thirty-six deaths and five hundred cases of liver and kidney damage.

Now comes a ripple of books that, were there any justice, would put a dozen or so hangdog executives in the dock. Three of the books make particularly persuasive cases. Paul Brodeur's *Outrageous Misconduct: The Asbestos Industry on Trial* (Pantheon) is an account of how the largest manufacturer of asbestos products, Manville Corporation (previously known as Johns-Manville Corporation), and other asbestos companies committed over the years what one plaintiff's attorney called "the greatest mass murder in history," which is possibly true if one means industrial mass murder, not political. People who regularly inhale asbestos fibers are likely to die, or at least be crippled, from the lung disease called asbestosis or the even worse (at least it sounds worse) mesthelioma. It sometimes takes twenty or thirty years for asbestosis to appear, so a measure of the slaughter from it is somewhat vague. But the best experts in the field, which means Dr. Irving J.

Selikoff and his staff at Mount Sinai Hospital in New York City, esti-
mate that aside from the many thousands who have died from
asbestos diseases in the past, there will be between eight and ten
thousand deaths from asbestos-related cancer each year for the next
twenty years. These deaths are not accidental. Manville et al. knew
exactly what they were doing. Brodeur's book is mainly an account of
how the asbestos companies, though they claimed to be ignorant of the
deadly quality of their product until a study by Dr. Selikoff was
released in 1964, had for forty years known about, and had suppressed or disregarded, hundreds of studies that clearly showed what
asbestos was doing to the people who inhaled it. Did the companies
even care what was happening? Typically, at a Manville asbestos mine
in Canada, company doctors found that of seven hundred and eight
workers, only four—who had worked there less than four years—had
normal lungs. Those who were dying of asbestosis were not told of
their ailment.

The other two books, Susan Perry and Jim Dawson's *Nightmare:
Women and the Dalkon Shield* (Macmillan) and Morton Mintz's *At Any
Cost: Corporate Greed, Women, and the Dalkon Shield* (Pantheon),
remind me of what Dr. Jules Amthor said to my favorite detective: "I'm
in a very sensitive profession, Mr. Marlowe. I'm a quack." The murder-
ous quackery of the Dalkon Shield, an intrauterine device, was committed by A.H. Robins, a company that should have stuck to making
Chap Stick and Sergeant's Flea & Tick Collars, and left birth-control
gadgets to those who knew how to make them properly. These two
books should convince anyone, I think, that compared to the fellows at
A.H. Robins, the Film Recovery executives were pikers when it came to
showing disregard for human lives for the sake of profits. Profits were
plentiful, that's for sure. A.H. Robins sold more than 4.5 million
Dalkon Shields worldwide (2.8 million in the United States) for $4.35
each; not bad for a device that cost only twenty-five cents to produce.
The death count among women who wore the shield still isn't complete; the last I heard it was twenty. But wearers of the shield also
have reported stillbirths, babies with major congenital defects, punctured uteri, forced hysterectomies, sterilization from infection, and
various tortures and illnesses by the thousands—some generous por-
tion, we may presume, of the 9230 lawsuits that A.H. Robins has settled out of court. And as both books make clear, the company launched
the Dalkon Shield fully aware of the shield's dangers, sold it with false

advertising, kept on selling it for several years after the company knew what its customers were going through, and pulled a complicated cover-up of guilt.

Dershowitz is right in one respect: corporate murderers are not like your typical killer on death row. Corporate murderers do not set out to kill. There's no profit in that. They are simply willing to accept a certain amount of death and physical torment among their workers and customers as a sometimes necessary byproduct of the free enterprise system. Mintz has uncovered a dandy quote from history to illustrate this attitude. When it was suggested to Alfred P. Sloan, Jr., president of General Motors circa 1930, that he should have safety glass installed in Chevrolets, he refused with the explanation, "Accidents or no accidents, my concern in this matter is a matter of profit and loss."

The Sloan spirit is everywhere. Brodeur quotes from a deposition of Charles H. Roemer, once a prominent New Jersey attorney who handled legal matters for the Union Asbestos and Rubber Company. Roemer reveals that around 1942, when Union Asbestos discovered a lot of its workers coming down with asbestos disease, he and some of Union Asbestos's top officials went to Johns-Manville and asked Vandiver Brown, Manville's attorney, and Lewis Brown, president of Manville, if their physical examination program had turned up similar results. According to Roemer, Vandiver Brown said, in effect, Sure, our X-rays show many of our workers have that disease, but we don't tell them they are sick because if we did, they would stop working and sue us. Roemer recalled asking, "Mr. Brown, do you mean to tell me you would let them work until they dropped dead?" and Brown answering, "Yes, we save a lot of money that way."

Saving money, along with making money, was obviously the paramount objective of A.H. Robins, too. This was evident from the beginning, when Robins officials learned—*six months before marketing the device nationally*—that the Dalkon Shield's multifilament tail had a wicking tendency and could carry potentially deadly bacteria into the uterus. Did the company hold up marketing the shield until it could be further tested and made safe? No, no. That would have meant a delay, for one thing, in recovering the $750 000 they had paid the shield's inventors. Though Robins knew it was putting its customers in great jeopardy, it hustled the shield onto the market with promotional claims that it was "safe" and "superior" to all other intrauterine devices; and, never, during the four years the shield was on the market, did A.H. Robins conduct wicking studies of the string. The shield's promotional literature, by the way, was a classic example of phony drugstore hype. A.H. Robins claimed the shield kept the pregnancy rate at 1.1 percent; the company was well aware that the shield allowed at least a 5 percent pregnancy rate, one of the most slipshod in the birth-control business. A.H. Robins also advertised that the device could be easily inserted in "even the most sensitive women," although in fact many doctors, before inserting the shield, had to give patients an anesthetic, and many women were in pain for months.

Not long after the shield went on the market, Wayne Crowder, one of the few heroes in this sorry tale, a quality-control engineer at Chap Stick, which manufactured many of the shields for its parent firm, rejected 10 000 of them because he was convinced the strings could wick bacteria. His boss overruled him with the remark, "Your conscience doesn't pay your salary." Crowder also suggested a method for stopping the wicking, but his technique was rejected because it would have cost an extra five cents per device. Crowder kept on complaining (he would ultimately be fired as an irritant) and he finally stirred Daniel French, president of Chap Stick, to convey Crowder's criticisms to the home office. French was told to mind his own business and not worry about the safety of the shield, which prompted him to go into the corporate softshoe routine he knew would please. He wrote A.H. Robins: "It is not the intention of Chap Stick Company to attempt any unauthorized improvements in the Dalkon Shield. My only interest in the Dalkon Shield is to produce it at the lowest possible price and, therefore, increase Robins' gross profit level."

Of course, when thousands of women begin dying, screaming, cursing, and suing, it gets a little difficult to pretend that all is well with one's product, but for more than a decade, A.H. Robins did its best, never recalling the gadget, never sending a warning to doctors about possible deadly side effects, and continuing to the last—continuing right up to the present even after losing hundreds of millions of dollars in lawsuits—to argue that the shield is just hunky-dory. The A.H. Robins school spirit was beautifully capsulated by one of its officials who told the *National Observer*, "But after all, we are in business to sell the thing, to make a profit. I don't mean we're trying to go out and sell products that are going to be dangerous, fatal, or what have you. But you don't put all the bad things in big headlines."

Where is the corporate executive who will not savor the easy insouciance of "or what have you"?

One of the more fascinating characteristics of corporate murderers is the way these fellows cover up their dirty work. They are really quite bold and successful in their deviousness. When one considers how many top officials there are at places like Manville and Robins, and when one assumes (obviously naïvely) among the lot of them surely there must be at least one or two with a functioning conscience, the completeness of their cover-ups is indeed impressive. Which isn't to say that their techniques are very sophisticated. They simply lie, or hide or burn the incriminating material. When the litigation flood began to break over Manville Corporation in the late 1960s, the asbestos gang began thwarting their victims' attorneys by claiming certain Manville executives couldn't give depositions because they were dead (when they were very much alive), by refusing to produce documents ordered by the court, and by denying that certain documents existed when in fact they did. A.H. Robins was just as expert at that sort of thing. According to Mintz, "Thousands of documents sought by lawyers for victims of the Dalkon Shield sank from sight in suspicious circumstances. A few were hidden for a decade in a home basement in Tulsa, Oklahoma. Other records were destroyed, some admittedly in a city dump in Columbus, Indiana, and some allegedly in an A.H. Robins furnace. And despite court orders, the company did not produce truckloads of documents for judicial rulings on whether the women's lawyers could see the papers."

A.H. Robins's most notorious effort at a cover-up ultimately failed, thanks to one Roger Tuttle, a classic example of what can happen when the worm turns.

Tuttle was an attorney for A.H. Robins in the early 1970s. He says that immediately after the company lost its first Dalkon Shield lawsuit, his superiors ordered him (they deny it) to search through the company's files and burn every document that he thought might be used against A.H. Robins in future lawsuits—documents that, in Tuttle's words, indicated "knowledge and complicity, if any, of top officials in what at that stage of the game appeared to be a grim situation." Unfortunately for the company, Tuttle did not fully obey orders. He took possession of some of the juiciest documents and kept them. Just why he rebelled isn't clear. Perhaps it was because Tuttle, a plain little guy who admits he isn't the smartest attorney in the world, was tired of having his employers push him around, which they often did. He says he did it because he was ashamed that "I personally lacked the courage" to challenge the order and "I wanted some sop for my own conscience as an attorney." Whatever his motivation, Tuttle sat on the purloined files for nearly ten years. He moved on to other jobs, finally winding up, a born-again Christian, on the Oral Roberts University law faculty. Watching the Dalkon Shield trials from afar, troubled by the plaintiffs' inability to cope with A.H. Robins's cover-up, Tuttle finally decided to step forward and provide the material their attorneys needed for the big breakthrough.

A lucky windfall like that is the only way victims can overcome the tremendous imbalance in legal firepower. In the way they muster defense, corporate murderers bear no resemblance to the broken-down, half-nuts, penniless drifters on death row, dozens of whom have no attorney at all. Corporate killers are like the Mafia in the way they come to court with a phalanx of attorneys. They are fronted by the best, or at least the best known. Griffin Bell, President Carter's Attorney General, has been one of A.H. Robins's attorneys.

There are two other significant differences between corporate killers and the habitués of death rows. In the first place, the latter generally did not murder as part of doing business, except for the relatively few who killed coincidental to a holdup. They did not murder to protect their rackets or territory, as the Mafia does, and they did not murder to exploit a patent or to increase production and sales, as corporate murderers do. One judge accused A.H. Robins officials of taking "the bottom line as your guiding beacon and the low road as your route." Killing for the bottom line has probably not sent a single murderer to death row anywhere. In the second place, most of the men and women on death row were lonely murderers. No part of society supported what they did. But just as the Mafia can commit murder with impunity only because it has the cooperation of police and prosecutors, so too corporate murderers benefit from the collusion of respectable professions, particularly doctors (who, for a price, keep quiet), and insurance companies (who, to Manville, did not reveal what their actuarial tables told about the risks to asbestos workers; and, for Robins, worked actively backstage to conceal the Dalkon Shield's menace to public health), and government agencies who are supposed to protect public health but look the other way.

It was an old, and in its way valid, excuse that Film Recovery's officials gave the court: "We were just operating like other plants, and none of the government health and safety inspectors who dropped around—neither the Elm Grove Village Public Health Department nor the Environmental Protection Agency—told us we shouldn't be letting our workers stick their heads in vats of boiling cyanide." They were probably telling the truth. That's the way health and safety regulations have usually operated.

Brodeur tells us that a veritable parade of government inspectors marched through the Pittsburgh Corning asbestos plants in Tyler, Texas, over a period of six and a half years without warning the workers that the asbestos dust levels were more than twenty times the maximum recommended for health safety. One Department of Labor official later admitted he had not worn a respirator when inspecting the plant because he did not want to excite the workers into asking questions about their health. Though the Public Health Service several times measured the fallout of asbestos dust, never did it warn the workers that the stuff was eating up their lungs. Finally things got so bad at Tyler that federal inspectors, forced to bring charges against the owners for appalling infractions of health standards, recommended that they be fined $210. Today the men and women who worked in that plant (since closed) are dying of lung cancer at a rate five times greater than the national average.

The most impressive bureaucratic collusion A.H. Robins received was, not surprisingly, from the Food and Drug Administration. When trial attorneys brought evidence that the Dalkon Shield's rotting tail strings were endangering thousands of women and asked FDA officials to remove the device from the market, the agency did nothing. When the National Women's Health Network petitioned the FDA for a recall—paid for by Robins—that would remove the shield from all women then wearing it, the FDA did nothing. For a full decade it pretended to be helpless.

There is one more significant difference between the people on death row and the corporate murderers: the former sometimes say they are sorry; the latter never do. Midway through 1985, Texas executed Charles Milton, thirty-four, because when he stuck up a liquor store the owner and his wife wrestled Milton for the gun, it went off, and the woman died. Shortly before the state killed him with poison,

Milton said, "I am sorry Mrs. Denton was killed in the struggle over the gun." There. He said it. It wasn't much, but he said it. And that's more than the folks at Manville have ever said about the thousands of people they killed with asbestos. When it comes to feeling no remorse, A.H. Robins doesn't take a back seat to anybody. In a famous courtroom confrontation between Federal Judge Miles W. Lord and three A.H. Robins officials, including company president E. Claiborne Robins, Jr., Judge Lord asked them to read silently to themselves a long reprimand of their actions.... Judge Lord admitted that he did not have the power to make them recall the shield but he begged them to do it on their own: "You've got lives out there, people, women, wives, moms, and some who will never be moms....You are the corporate conscience. Please, in the name of humanity, lift your eyes above the bottom line."

It was a pretty stirring piece of writing (later, when Judge Lord got so angry he read it aloud, they say half the courtroom was in tears), and the judge asked them if it had had any impact on them.

Looking sulky, they just stared at him and said nothing.

A few weeks later, at A.H. Robins's annual meeting, E. Claiborne Robins, Jr., dismissed Lord's speech as a "poisonous attack." The company did not recall the shield for another eight months.

Giving deposition in 1984, Ernest L. Bender, Jr., senior vice-president for corporate planning and development, was asked if he had ever heard an officer or employee say he or she was "sorry or remorseful about any infection that's been suffered by any Dalkon Shield wearer." He answered, "I've never head anyone make such remarks because I've never heard anyone that said the Dalkon Shield was the cause."

What punishment is fitting for these fellows?

If they are murderers, why not the death sentence? Polls show that eighty-four percent of Americans favor the death penalty, but half think the penalty is unfairly applied. Let's restore their faith by applying justice equally and poetically. In Georgia recently it took the state two 2080 volts spaced over nineteen minutes to kill a black man who murdered during a burglary. How fitting it would be to use the same sort of defective electric chair to execute, for example, auto manufacturers and tire manufacturers who knowingly kill people with defective merchandise. In Texas recently it took the state executioners forty minutes to administer the lethal poison to a drifter who had killed a woman. Could anything be more appropriate that to tie down drug and device manufacturers who have killed many women and let slow-witted executioners poke around their bodies for an hour or so, looking for just the right blood vessel to transport the poison? At a recent Mississippi execution, the prisoner's protracted gasping for breath became such an ugly spectacle that prison authorities, in a strange burst of decorum, ordered witnesses out of the death chamber. That sort of execution for Manville executives who specialized in spreading long-term asphyxiation over thousands of lives would certainly be appropriate.

But these things will never happen. For all of our popular declarations of democracy, most Americans are such forelock-tugging toadies that they would be horrified to see, say, Henry Ford II occupying the same electric chair that cooked black, penniless, Alpha Otis Stephens.

Nor will we incarcerate many corporate murderers. Though some of us with a mean streak may enjoy fantasizing the reception that our fat-assed corporate killers would get from some of their cellmates in America's more interesting prisons—I like to think of the pious chaps from A.H. Robins spending time in Tennessee's notorious Brushy Mountain Prison—that is not going to happen very often either, the precedent of Film Recovery to the contrary notwithstanding. The Film Recovery trio had the misfortune of working for a crappy little corporation that has since gone defunct. Judges will not be so stern with killers from giant corporations.

So long as we have an army of crassly aggressive plaintiff attorneys to rely on, however, there is always the hope that we can smite the corporations and the men who run them with a punishment they probably fear worse than death or loss of freedom: to wit, massive loss of profits. Pamela C. Van Duyn, whose use of the Dalkon Shield at the age of twenty-six destroyed one Fallopian tube and critically damaged the other (her childbearing chances are virtually nil), says: "As far as I'm concerned, the last dime that is in Claiborne Robins's pocket ought to be paid over to all the people that have suffered."...

As it became evident that juries were inclined to agree with Mrs. Van Duyn's proposal to wring plenty of money from A.H. Robins, the corporation in 1985 sought protection under Chapter 11 of the Federal Bankruptcy Code. It was a sleazy legal trick they had picked up from Manville Corporation, which had declared bankruptcy in August 1982.

Although both corporations lost hundreds of millions in court fights, neither was actually in financial trouble. Indeed, at the time it copped out under Chapter 11, Manville was the nation's 181st largest corporation and had assets of more than $2 billion. Bankruptcy was a transparent ploy—or, as plaintiff attorneys put it, a fraudulent abuse and perversion of the bankruptcy laws—but with the connivance of the federal courts it is a ploy that has worked. Not a penny has been paid to the victims of either corporation since they declared bankruptcy, and the 16 500 pending lawsuits against Manville and the 5000 lawsuits pending against A.H. Robins (those figures are climbing every day) have been frozen.

Meanwhile, companies are not even mildly chastised. Quite the contrary. Most major newspapers have said nothing about Manville's malevolent cover-up but have clucked sympathetically over its courtroom defeats. *The New York Times* editorially seemed to deplore the financial problems of the asbestos industry almost as much as it deplored the industry's massacre of workers: "Asbestos is a tragedy, most of all for the victims and their families but also for the companies, which are being made to pay the price for decisions made long ago." Senator Gary Hart, whose home state, Colorado, is corporate headquarters for Manville, pitched in with legislation that would lift financial penalty from the asbestos companies and dump it on the taxpayers. And in Richmond, Virginia, corporate headquarters for the makers of the Dalkon Shield, civic leaders threw a banquet for E. Claiborne Robins, Sr. The president of the University of Virginia assured Robins that "Your example will cast its shadow into eternity, as the sands of time carry the indelible footprint of your good works. We applaud you for always exhibiting a steadfast and devoted concern for your fellow man. Truly, the Lord has chosen you as one of His most essential instruments."

After similar encomiums from other community leaders, the top man behind the marketing of the Dalkon Shield was given the Great American Tradition Award.

Portrait of a Machine

BY

LOUIS

UNTERMEYER

What nudity is beautiful as this
Obedient monster purring at its toil;
These naked iron muscles dripping oil;
And the sure-fingered rods that never miss.
This long and shiny flank of metal is
Magic that greasy labor cannot spoil;
While this vast engine that could rend the soil
Conceals its fury with a gentle hiss.

It does not vent its loathing, does not turn
Upon its makers with destroying hate.
It bears a deeper malice; throbs to earn
Its master's bread and lives to see this great
Lord of the earth, who rules but cannot learn,
Become the slave of what his slaves create.

Chicken and Fingers

BY
MARY
MAXWELL

The names of the women in this essay have been changed because of the content of the material and the very real threat to the employees of losing their jobs.

ophie's right hand has tightened into a permanent claw. Olga has developed a chronic misalignment of her spine and Florence now has one hand that's significantly larger than the other. Mildred's grip will never be normal again. As for Sonya, her wrists have literally worn out. These are just some of the exploited women I came to know when I was hired to open a health office in a meat-packing plant outside a prairie city.

The workers I met there belong to a silent majority numbering many thousands; women who are violated daily by the crippling work they must do to make a living. Despite permanent injury, daily pain, and frequent harassment at work, they rarely complain aloud for fear of losing their jobs.

This packing plant was opened in the late eighties, and management claimed its design and equipment was "state of the art." Production moved here from an older plant in the downtown area. Now, it was in the suburbs.

When the new plant opened, the company reasoned that hiring a nurse like me to work on the premises would help control absenteeism, rising compensation claims, and resulting fines. The legally required assessment of employees who worked directly with the product would be done at the plant rather than giving workers time off to seek treatment elsewhere.

For years the meat-packing industry has been at the top of the Department of Labour's list of hazardous industries. As an article in the *New York Times* described a few years ago, workers in a packing plant toil in extreme heat or refrigerated cold; they stand shoulder to shoulder on assembly lines for hours wielding honed knives and power saws. Grease and blood make the floor slippery and the roar of machines is constant. There is an overpowering stench from the offal. I saw the workers cut themselves, slip, fall. They wore out their insides doing repetitive-motion jobs. In this plant the annual statistics showed that out of every one hundred workers there were about thirty work-related injuries and illnesses. This is roughly four times the average in private industry.

The plant manager told me part of my job would be to tour the work site regularly and watch the workers do their jobs so I would better understand the problems brought to the health office. When I advised him that part of my duty as a health professional was to guard a person's confidentiality about health findings or personal problems, he said, "Of course," and so I should. However, if a person's problem interfered with her work, he reminded me, there were a lot of others out there who could replace her.

The plant tour began at the receiving area, where trucks stacked high with crates of live poultry waited to be unloaded. On the platform, two men lifted crates of ten to fifteen live chickens on a moving belt that led to the "live hangers" who opened the crates and hung each of the chickens by one foot on a moving chain, which then carried them to the "sticker," who slit the chickens' throats after they had been electrocuted in a water bath. The chain carried the dead chickens through machines that plucked and singed feathers, cut off the heads and feet. Then two men, the "dead hangers," hung them on another chain that carried them into the eviscerating room. Here the entrails were removed by a combination of machines and human labour.

Fifteen people worked in this room, which swirled with steam so thick you could not see across it; the temperature was roughly 29° Celsius and the noise was deafening. An overwhelming stench hung in the hot, heavy air. Ten of the people in this room were women, all of them over fifty.

As I interviewed each person in my office during the health assessments, I was struck with the number of these women whose extremities had become permanently disabled from their work on the assembly line. At first glance, they appeared normal; that is, they could walk and use their limbs in most activities of daily living. However, their hands in particular were visibly distorted, raw, and work-worn.

Sophie had worked in the eviscerating room for twenty-one years, pulling guts with her right hand; it had become larger than her left and had tightened into a permanent claw because of the repetitive nature of this job. This made it impossible for her to wear gloves—a change I attempted to introduce in this area. She could not straighten her fingers nor could she touch each finger with her thumb. It was as if her hand was frozen in this position: when she removed her glasses to clean off the spatters of blood, she grabbed them with her claw-like hand and pulled them sideways off her face. Sophie stood on a metal platform and yanked the chicken's guts, which had been mechanically pulled to the outside of the carcass before it reached her. Her back had grown a hump of muscle between her shoulders from twenty years of leaning forward to pull guts. Her fingernails were embedded with fungus, cracked and misshapen. The skin on her hands was thin and broken in several places, and there was evidence of many old wounds. She had tortuous varicose veins in her swollen legs from standing, her ankles bulging over her shoes.

When I saw Sophie in my office she was quiet, speaking little of her family or about the sure ache in her hands and legs. She was short and rotund—her hair bleach-blonde—and when she smiled her plump cheeks framed a nearly toothless grin. Sophie was not interested in trying another job to give her back and hands a rest. She said she was not long from retirement and besides, she was used to her job and thought she did it well.

Olga, known as Ollie, had worked on the gizzard-harvesting machine for nineteen years. She sat on a metal stool hunched over a table, sweat dripping down from her glasses. With her right hand she grabbed the mechanically removed gizzard fed to her by an auger, snipped it in half, peeled it and then pushed it through a hole on her table that carried the gizzards to another part of the plant. Her left hand was covered with warts and several cuts in various stages of healing. The warts were caused by bacteria from the chickens, the cuts from the scissors slipping. Because of the design of her work station, she was required to sit on a high stool with no back support so she walked with a permanent forward stoop. She had headaches daily from the chronic misalignment of her spine and neck. Her vision had deteriorated because of the close work and poor lighting. She had a significant hearing loss from the years of working in noise without proper hearing protection.

Ollie visited me daily, always with a cheerful message and a wink even when asking for an aspirin. In her calm, rather resigned manner she expressed concern for some of the younger women's work-related health problems but minimized her own. Ollie talked about her sixteen grandchildren, of frequent weddings and birthdays, and how she regularly knitted clothing and made perogies for them. I wondered how she could smoothly roll out the perogy dough with such misshapen hands.

Florence had worked on the line for twelve years as a checker. It was her job to examine the eviscerated birds for any bruises or obvious malformations before they reached the inspectors from Agriculture Canada. She stood for the entire shift and wore a wire mesh glove on her left hand to grab the bird by the leg. With her right hand she slashed a large sharp knife through the diseased or bruised bone or muscle, marking it as unfit. The line moved at 42 birds a minute or 2520 an hour. Some days the kill was twenty-four thousand. On a busy day, Florence made over seven thousand slashing movements with her right hand; consequently, it was significantly larger than her left. She had an unusual muscle mass just above the wrist on her right arm from the repetitive motion; across her shoulders and up into her neck was a thick ledge of knotted muscle that caused her constant pain.

When I tried to massage her shoulders, it felt like kneading cement. After two sessions, Florence said she could not stand the pain during and after the massage. Her normal posture was to keep her shoulders hunched up around her ears rather than relax them; consequently any relaxation induced by the massage was painful. She also had a persistent problem with fungus growing in her outer ear. One day on the line, she had scratched the ear with her gloved hand and even though she'd had a course of antibiotics, it still bothered her.

It took time to win Florence's confidence, as she was extremely suspicious of me. I had to prove I was not a spy for management. When I had, she would come in after her shift and in a deep and serious voice, sometimes almost whispering for fear of being overheard, she would lean toward me and tell me some of the problems she saw as a worker at the plant. She believed management was slowly replacing women with men because, as she put it, men don't wear out so quickly; she said the soap at the hand-washing stations was watered down (to save money), so workers never really felt their hands were clean; she said the knives were cheap and never sharpened properly and it was easier to cut yourself because of this. Flo suggested her back might not hurt so much—especially after the roasters went through (they were larger than the small fryers usually processed) —if she and the other workers could have one metal stool to take turns sitting down. All of her concerns had been brought to the attention of her foreman, she said, but he just told her to stop complaining.

Florence's husband was a trucker, so she had raised her family on her own and spoke with great pride about her children. She talked of someday quitting the job and applying to shelter homeless, retarded adults. She said she just loved those people.

Mildred was a checker too, there for about the same number of years. Both of her wrists had gone, as she put it, again from the repetitive motion required by her job. And even though she had had surgery on them in order to free the nerve, her grip was that of a child. Millie wondered if she could get them "done again" so she could continue her job. I told her the details about carpal tunnel syndrome, explaining her wrists would never be the same again, even after surgery. As with many others who had to miss time because of a work-related injury or illness, Millie was docked sick time when she was off for surgery instead of being covered by Workers' Compensation.

The exact date of a repetitive strain injury is difficult to ascertain and to be awarded compensation benefits, the date and time of injury has to be given and supported by the employers. Workers' claims were repeatedly refuted by management; thus the person was denied benefits and had to use sick time for an injury very clearly caused at and by work. (Although this was five years ago, both management and this policy remain unchanged.)

Mildred played bingo almost every night, hoping to win someday so she could quit her job.

During the working day at coffee or lunch break the women would sit together in groups in the coffee room, pass around pictures of recent family events, play a hand or two of rummy while they absentmindedly rubbed their hurting parts, wipe the smear of chicken blood and bile from their glasses and tell jokes. One would warble hymns such as "Amazing Grace" and "Rock of Ages" in sweet soprano while another hummed country and western ballads. They exchanged endless stories about bingo, wondering aloud when they might win the big one.

Next to the eviscerating room was the pack room. Out of the thirty people who worked there, twenty were women. Here the eviscerated chicken was cooled in large refrigerated tanks and then dismembered with a series of cuts either by machine or by hand, each person performing the same motion over and over again for up to twelve hours a day. The temperature was kept cool at 10° Celsius to discourage bacteria from growing on the raw chicken. Most of the people worked with felt liners inside their hard hats and double wool socks inside rubber boots to insulate them from the cold concrete floor. Here the women were younger, most in their twenties, single, and with young children.

Sonya had worked at the plant for four years on the electric saw, cutting the chicken into nine pieces. Soon after I arrived she was unable to work in this area because her wrists had literally worn out. She was twenty-two. After her doctor demanded she be taken off the saw, Sonya was constantly harassed by the packroom foreman, who verbally abused and humiliated her because he did not believe she was really disabled. He was convinced she just did not want to work. The jobs he assigned her, even though they were supposed to be easier, required her to keep flexing her wrists, which had caused her problems in the first place. He also cut her hours and would not allow her to leave the floor to go to the washroom.

Two older women, Lizzie and Ann, were both close to retirement and had disabling medical problems as a result of their jobs. They had grown bitter from years of abuse and poor working conditions, despite the efforts of the union and promises from management that things would change after they moved to the new plant. Ann's husband had a brain tumour and was in a chronic care home. She was trying to put her son through university. Lizzie's husband had to quit his job at the plant after thirty-two years as he was unable to work on the vacuum machine because of a frozen left shoulder caused by overuse in this very job. He was denied Worker's Compensation because he had been in an accident about the same time he was experiencing problems with his shoulder, and the plant claimed he had never complained about his shoulder before the accident. They had difficulty making it on Lizzie's salary.

Some days when the foreman had been chewed out by the production manager because efficiency rates and production quotas were down, he would speed up the line and cause an increase in accidents and injuries. The people on the line would plead with him to slow it down but he would just stare at them, almost threatening to increase it some more. He was in the middle of a divorce and had just found out that he had lost custody of his son because of his drinking.

Most of the people at the plant were poorly educated and had come up the hard way. Their identities were tied to their jobs; they were grateful for work and had an unswerving loyalty to the company. They put up with the poor working conditions, mistreatment, and abuse because they did not believe they could get another job. They said they got used to going home hurting.

I found the conditions in this new plant to be outdated and horrifying. All my attempts to negotiate with management to change some of the more grisly conditions failed. I learned that the business of packing meat was a brutal industry whose dominant corporate ideology was to blame the victim. I saw the worker set up as a culprit, seen as careless or accident-prone, freeing the company or work environment from responsibility. Often the poor equipment design, inadequate ventilation, and lack of management directives (such as job rotation) caused accidents and resulted in the company paying fines for having compensation costs that were far higher than in other industries.

I heard management say, "If she hadn't been so careless," and "I told her to wear a mesh glove; she wouldn't listen, so she was asking for it." But there were no mesh gloves to fit her because someone forgot to order them. And her so-called carelessness was caused by cheap knives that could not keep an edge. It was disturbing that management's statements echoed what we often hear in rape cases.

For the first few weeks working in this plant I was in a state of shock. I have never seen people used up and abused on such a large scale. At first I found their complacency and powerlessness contemptible, but slowly I began to understand that if they kept quiet the abuse would not escalate as it did when someone asked for change. I was not able to change any of the abominable conditions for these people but by taking the time to listen and by believing what they were saying about the horror in their lives, I was able to validate their experience and some of them actually came to believe they deserved a better place to work and left.

Working women are on the lowest rung of the job ladder. This, in addition to their poverty, low self-image, and poor education, is exploited in workplaces such as this one. Unlike their articulate sisters in business, the professions, and academia, they have yet to find their public voice. Yet their plight demands to be heard.

Ever since I worked in this packing plant, I have wanted to describe what I saw and heard. I hope this story will encourage others to tell the truth about what is happening in many working environments across Canada. The conditions I encountered in one plant—and comparable conditions in who knows how many other similar workplaces—are not all that different from the barbaric conditions Upton Sinclair exposed in his epic novel of Chicago meat-packing plants, *The Jungle*. That book was written almost one hundred years ago.

Time and Motion Study

BY

ADRIAN

MITCHELL

Slow down the film. You see that bit.
Seven days old and no work done.
Two hands clutching nothing but air,
Two legs kicking nothing but air.
That yell. There's wasted energy there.
No use to himself, no good for the firm.
Make a note of that.

New film. Now look, now he's fourteen.
Work out the energy required
To make him grow that tall.
It could have been used
It could have all been used
For the good of the firm and he could have stayed small.
Make a note of that.

Age thirty. And the waste continues.
Using his legs for walking. Tiring
His mouth with talking and eating. Twitching.
Slow it down. Reproducing? I see.
All, I suppose, for the good of the firm.
But he'd better change methods. Yes, he'd better.
Look at the waste of time and emotion.
Look at the waste. Look. Look.
And make a note of that.

Action
Will Be Taken

An Action-packed Story

~

BY HEINRICH BÖLL

Translated by Leila Vennewitz

robably one of the strangest interludes in my life was the time I
spent as an employee in Alfred Wunsiedel's factory. By nature I
am inclined more to pensiveness and inactivity than to work, but
now and again prolonged financial difficulties compel me—for pensiveness is no more profitable than inactivity—to take on a so-called
job. Finding myself once again at a low ebb of this kind, I put myself in
the hands of the employment office and was sent with seven other fellow-sufferers to Wunsiedel's factory, where we were to undergo an
aptitude test.

The exterior of the factory was enough to arouse my suspicions:
the factory was built entirely of glass brick, and my aversion to well-lit
buildings and well-lit rooms is as strong as my aversion to work. I
became even more suspicious when we were immediately served
breakfast in the well-lit, cheerful coffee shop: pretty waitresses
brought us eggs, coffee and toast, orange juice was served in tastefully
designed jugs, goldfish pressed their bored faces against the sides of
pale-green aquariums. The waitresses were so cheerful that they
appeared to be bursting with good cheer. Only a strong effort of will—
so it seemed to me—restrained them from singing away all day long.

They were as crammed with unsung songs as chickens with unlaid eggs.

Right away I realized something that my fellow-sufferers evidently failed to realize: that this breakfast was already part of the test; so I chewed away reverently, with the full appreciation of a person who knows he is supplying his body with valuable elements. I did something which normally no power on earth can make me do: I drank orange juice on an empty stomach, left the coffee and egg untouched, as well as most of the toast, got up, and paced up and down in the coffee shop, pregnant with action.

As a result I was the first to be ushered into the room where the questionnaires were spread out on attractive tables. The walls were done in a shade of green that would have summoned the word "delightful" to the lips of interior decoration enthusiasts. The room appeared to be empty, and yet I was so sure of being observed that I behaved as someone pregnant with action behaves when he believes himself unobserved: I ripped my pen impatiently from my pocket, unscrewed the top, sat down at the nearest table and pulled the questionnaire toward me, the way irritable customers snatch at the bill in a restaurant.

Question No. 1: Do you consider it right for a human being to possess only two arms, two legs, eyes, and ears?

Here for the first time I reaped the harvest of my pensive nature and wrote without hesitation: "Even four arms, legs and ears would not be adequate for my driving energy. Human beings are very poorly equipped."

Question No. 2: How many telephones can you handle at one time?

Here again the answer was as easy as simple arithmetic: "When there are only seven telephones," I wrote, "I get impatient; there have to be nine before I feel I am working to capacity."

Question No. 3: How do you spend your free time?

My answer: "I no longer acknowledge the term free time—on my fifteenth birthday I eliminated it from my vocabulary, for in the beginning was the act."

I got the job. Even with nine telephones I really didn't feel I was working to capacity. I shouted into the mouth-pieces: "Take immediate action!" or: "Do something!—We must have some action—Action will be taken—Action has been taken—Action should be taken." But as a rule—for I felt this was in keeping with the tone of the place—I used the imperative.

Of considerable interest were the noon-hour breaks, when we consumed nutritious foods in an atmosphere of silent good cheer. Wunsiedel's factory was swarming with people who were obsessed with telling you the story of their lives, as indeed vigorous personalities are fond of doing. The story of their lives is more important to them than their lives, you have only to press a button, and immediately it is covered with spewed-out exploits.

Wunsiedel had a right-hand man called Broschek, who had in turn made a name for himself by supporting seven children and a paralyzed wife by working night-shifts in his student days, and successfully carrying on four business agencies, besides which he had passed two examinations with honors in two years. When asked by reporters: "When do you sleep, Mr. Broschek?" he had replied: "It's a crime to sleep!"

Wunsiedel's secretary had supported a paralyzed husband and four children by knitting, at the same time graduating in psychology and German history as well as breeding shepherd dogs, and she had become famous as a night-club singer where she was known as *Vamp Number Seven.*

Wunsiedel himself was one of those people who every morning, as they open their eyes, make up their minds to act. "I must act," they think as they briskly tie their bathrobe belts around them. "I must act," they think as they shave, triumphantly watching their beard hairs being washed away with the lather: these hirsute vestiges are the first daily sacrifices to their driving energy. The more intimate functions also give these people a sense of satisfaction: water swishes, paper is used. Action has been taken. Bread gets eaten, eggs are decapitated.

With Wunsiedel, the most trivial activity looked like action: the way he put on his hat, the way—quivering with energy—he buttoned up his overcoat, the kiss he gave his wife, everything was action.

When he arrived at his office he greeted his secretary with a cry of "Let's have some action!" And in ringing tones she would call back: "Action will be taken!" Wunsiedel then went from department to department, calling out his cheerful: "Let's have some action!" Everyone would answer: "Action will be taken!" And I would call back to him too, with a radiant smile, when he looked into my office: "Action will be taken!"

Within a week I had increased the number of telephones on my desk to eleven, within two weeks to thirteen, and every morning on the streetcar I enjoyed thinking up new imperatives, or chasing the words *take action* through various tenses and modulations: for two whole days I kept saying the same sentence over and over again because I thought it sounded so marvelous: "Action ought to have been taken;" for another two days it was: "Such action ought not to have been taken."

So I was really beginning to feel I was working to capacity when there actually was some action. One Tuesday morning—I had hardly settled down at my desk—Wunsiedel rushed into my office crying his "Let's have some action!" But an inexplicable something in his face made me hesitate to reply, in a cheerful gay voice as the rules dictated: "Action will be taken!" I must have paused too long, for Wunsiedel, who seldom raised his voice, shouted at me: "Answer! Answer, you know the rules!" And I answered, under my breath, reluctantly, like a child who is forced to say: I am a naughty child. It was only by a great effort that I managed to bring out the sentence: "Action will be taken," and hardly had I uttered it when there really was some action: Wunsiedel dropped to the floor. As he fell he rolled over onto his side and lay right across the open doorway. I knew at once, and I confirmed it when I went slowly around my desk and approached the body on the floor: he was dead.

Shaking my head I stepped over Wunsiedel, walked slowly along the corridor to Broschek's office, and entered without knocking. Broschek was sitting at his desk, a telephone receiver in each hand, between his teeth a ballpoint pen with which he was making notes on a writing pad, while with his bare feet he was operating a knitting machine under the desk. In this way he helps to clothe his family. "We've had some action," I said in a low voice.

Broschek spat out the ballpoint pen, put down the two receivers, reluctantly detached his toes from the knitting machine.

"What action?" he asked.

"Wunsiedel is dead," I said.

"No," said Broschek.

"Yes," I said, "come and have a look!"

"No," said Broschek, "that's impossible," but he put on his slippers and followed me along the corridor.

"No," he said, when we stood beside Wunsiedel's corpse, "no, no!" I did not contradict him. I carefully turned Wunsiedel over onto his back, closed his eyes, and looked at him pensively.

I felt something like tenderness for him and realized for the first time that I had never hated him. On his face was that expression which one sees on children who obstinately refuse to give up their faith in Santa Claus, even though the arguments of their playmates sound so convincing.

"No," said Broschek, "no."

"We must take action," I said quietly to Broschek.

"Yes," said Broschek, "we must take action."

Action was taken: Wunsiedel was buried, and I was delegated to carry a wreath of artificial roses behind his coffin, for I am equipped with not only a penchant for pensiveness and inactivity but also a face and figure that go extremely well with dark suits. Apparently as I walked along behind Wunsiedel's coffin carrying the wreath of artificial roses I looked superb. I received an offer from a fashionable firm of funeral directors to join their staff as a professional mourner. "You are a born mourner," said the manager, "your outfit would be provided by the firm. Your face—simply superb!"

I handed in my notice to Broschek, explaining that I had never really felt I was working to capacity there; that, in spite of the thirteen telephones, some of my talents were going to waste. As soon as my first professional appearance as a mourner was over I knew: This is where I belong, this is what I am cut out for.

Pensively I stand behind the coffin in the funeral chapel, holding a simple bouquet, while the organ plays Handel's *Largo*, a piece that does not receive nearly the respect it deserves. The cemetery café is my regular haunt; there I spend the intervals between my professional engagements, although sometimes I walk behind coffins which I have not been engaged to follow, I pay for flowers out of my own pocket and join the welfare worker who walks behind the coffin of some homeless person. From time to time I also visit Wunsiedel's grave, for after all I owe it to him that I discovered my true vocation, a vocation in which pensiveness is essential and inactivity my duty.

It was not till much later that I realized I had never bothered to find out what was being produced in Wunsiedel's factory. I expect it was soap.

Ogun

BY

EDWARD

KAMAU

BRATHWAITE

Ogun: Yoruba and Afro-Caribbean Creator God,
seen here in his aspect of divine craftsman.

My uncle made chairs, tables, balanced doors on, dug out
coffins, smoothing the white wood out

with plane and quick sandpaper until
it shone like his short-sighted glasses.

The knuckles of his hands were sil-
vered knobs of nails hit, hurt and flat-

tened out with blast of heavy hammer. He was knock-knee'd, flat-
footed and his clip clop sandals slapped across the concrete

flooring of his little shop where canefield mulemen and a fleet
of Bedford lorry drivers dropped in to scratch themselves and talk.

There was no shock of wood, no beam
of light mahogany his saw teeth couldn't handle.

When shaping squares for locks, a key hole
care tapped rat tat tat upon the handle

of his humpbacked chisel. Cold
world of wood caught fire as he whittled: rectangle

window frames, the intersecting x of fold-
ing chairs, triangle

trellises, the donkey
box-cart in its squeaking square.

But he was poor and most days he was hungry.
Imported cabinets with mirrors, formica table

tops, spine-curving chairs made up of tubes, with hollow
steel-like bird bones that sat on rubber ploughs,

thin beds, stretched not on boards, but blue high-tensioned cables,
were what the world preferred.

And yet he had a block of wood that would have baffled them.
With knife and gimlet care he worked away at this on Sundays,

explored its knotted hurts, cutting his way
along its yellow whorls until his hands could feel

how it had swelled and shivered, breathing air,
its weathered green burning to rings of time,

its contoured grain still tuned to roots and water.
And as he cut, he heard the creak of forests:

green lizard faces gulped, grey memories with moth
eyes watched him from their shadows, soft

liquid tendrils leaked among the flowers
and a black rigid thunder he had never heard within his hammer

came stomping up the trunks. And as he worked within his shattered
Sunday shop, the wood took shape: dry shuttered

eyes, slack anciently everted lips, flat
ruined face, eaten by pox, ravaged by rat

and woodworm, dry cistern mouth, cracked
gullet crying for the desert, the heavy black

enduring jaw; lost pain, lost iron;
emerging woodwork image of his anger.

Labours and Loves

BY

VAL

ROSS

Julie Voyce's answering machine says it all: "You have reached the operational headquarters of J. Voyce, cleaner of dirt, maker of things."

Voyce, a Toronto visual artist, had taken on cleaning jobs since 1982 but it wasn't until 1987 that she decided to ditch her various other part-time gigs and dedicate herself to the vacuum. "Ideally, you'd love to just make money off your art, but as a day job, I like it. The hours are flexible and it doesn't use your brain up. You can clean a house and, at the end of the day, you still have your thoughts." And a day spent cleaning leaves her eager to get back to her art, which she considers another advantage.

The 36-year-old artist works five days a week to earn $14 000 in a good year—80 per cent of her income. The rest she earns from her paintings, sculptures and the smaller, more affordable items like cardboard jewelry or dolls that she has recently started making under the label R.E.D.H.O.T. Productions.

If she could live off her art, she would give up cleaning, but very slowly—she would be loath to abandon long-time clients and if she weren't cleaning houses, she'd have to find some other way of getting exercise.

Bill Grove, 41, is a jazz musician (sax, guitar, piano) and leader of a five-piece band, Noise R Us. He also hosts a radio show, *What Is Jazz?* Neither gig pays. In fact, Grove says, "Playing jazz is a write-off. You know that joke about the jazz musician who wins the lottery and is asked what he's going to do with the money? He says, 'Oh, keep playing 'til it's gone.'" Grove says 75 per cent of his income comes from teaching—piano, sax and guitar at his place. He charges $40 an hour, "to ensure I get serious people."

Until recently, Grove supported his jazz habit by baking date squares and peddling them (literally—he delivered by bicycle) to health food stores. He reckons he baked more than 700 000: "I began to see little golden arches with date palms on them." Although he says the work had little obvious crossover for his jazz, "it let me work at home. I'm a home body, a hermit. And when I knew I had the date squares in the oven, it gave me a set time to practice: exactly 45 minutes. Better yet, I could make them at 2 in the morning."

Christine Slater, the author of a book of funky, sophisticated short stories *(Stalking the Gilded Boneyard)*, has been described as "a genuine mesmerist" by one reviewer. The 32-year-old mesmerist is by day organization development manager for a major manufacturer of paper products—toilet tissues and paper towels. "Technically," says Slater, "I've got responsibility for training 500-odd people who range from office staff and accountants to those operating the lines [conveyor belts] and running paper machines. We do everything here but grow the trees.

"There's no crossover with my writing, but I think that's healthy. It keeps my head in a different environment. It keeps me sane—though there would be those who would argue that." Slater joined her company right out of university, where she had majored in English. "I had a fairly useless arts degree, so it's been nice to succeed at something you weren't primed to do. And I do a lot of travelling, especially when I was in the recruiting arm of the company—places like Green Bay and Cincinnati. I can write as I travel."

Slater makes more than 50 times the income in her day job that she makes in writing, which in a good year—if she sells a couple of stories—may edge near the four-digit bracket.

Jack Micay makes award-winning documentaries on subjects ranging from the Sherpas of Nepal to the biological role of oxygen. He's also a practicing physician. Except for his hectic years as a medical intern and resident, Micay, 44, says he's been steadily involved in filmmaking since ending his undergraduate studies. But the film part of his life has been gradually edging out the medical part. For a while, it was a 50/50 split. Now he's down to working as a doctor about one day a week, in a downtown clinic.

"I used to work nights and weekends in hospital emergency rooms [and on films during the day]. Now the medicine is more part-time. I sort of regret I don't have more time to devote to it."

He says he obviously earns far more "per unit time" as a doctor, but that he now makes "several times as much" overall as a filmmaker/distributor than as a physician.

Since many of Micay's films have been based on scientific or medical subjects, there's obviously a degree of crossover. "I used to do documentaries on medical topics for the CBC, so I would usually learn something useful [for the practice of medicine]. Also, being a doctor sometimes helps me get access to people."

from

Writing Down the Bones

BY

NATALIE
GOLDBERG

Writing as a Practice

This is the practice school of writing. Like running, the more you do it, the better you get at it. Some days you don't want to run and you resist every step of the three miles, but you do it anyway. You practice whether you want to or not. You don't wait around for inspiration and a deep desire to run. It'll never happen, especially if you are out of shape and have been avoiding it. But if you run regularly, you train your mind to cut through or ignore your resistance. You just do it. And in the middle of the run, you love it. When you come to the end, you never want to stop. And you stop, hungry for the next time.

That's how writing is, too. Once you're deep into it, you wonder what took you so long to finally settle down at the desk. Through practice you actually do get better. You learn to trust your deep self more and not give in to your voice that wants to avoid writing. It is odd that we never question the feasibility of a football team practicing long hours for one game; yet in writing we rarely give ourselves the space for practice.

When you write, don't say, "I'm going to write a poem." That attitude will freeze you right away. Sit down with the least expectation of yourself; say, "I am free to write the worst junk in the world." You have to give yourself the space to write a lot without a destination. I've had students who said they decided they were going to write the great American novel and haven't written a line since. If every time you sat down, you expected something great, writing would always be a great disappointment. Plus that expectation would also keep you from writing.

My rule is to finish a notebook a month. (I'm always making up writing guidelines for myself.) Simply to fill it. That is the practice. My ideal is to write every day. I say it is my ideal. I am careful not to pass judgment or create anxiety if I don't do that. No one lives up to his ideal.

In my notebooks I don't bother with the side margin or the one at the top: I fill the whole page. I am not writing anymore for a teacher or for school. I am writing for myself first and I don't have to stay within my limits, not even margins. This gives me a psychological freedom and permission. And when my writing is on and I'm really cooking, I usually forget about punctuation, spelling, etc. I also notice that my handwriting changes. It becomes larger and looser.

Often I can look around the room at my students as they write and can tell which ones are really on and present at a given time in their writing. They are more intensely involved and their bodies are hanging loose. Again, it is like running. There's little resistance when the run is good. All of you is moving; there's no you separate from the runner. In writing, when you are truly on, there's no writer, no paper, no pen, no thoughts. Only writing does writing—everything else is gone.

One of the main aims in writing practice is to learn to trust your own mind and body; to grow patient and nonaggressive. Art lives in the Big World. One poem or story doesn't matter one way or the other. It's the process of writing and life that matters. Too many writers have written great books and gone insane or alcoholic or killed themselves. This process teaches about sanity. We are trying to become sane along with our poems and stories.

Chögyam Trungpa, Rinpoche, a Tibetan Buddhist master, said, "We must continue to open in the face of tremendous opposition. No one is encouraging us to open and still we must peel away the layers of the heart." It is the same with this way of practice writing: We must continue to open and trust in our own voice and process. Ultimately, if the process is good, the end will be good. You will get good writing.

A friend once said that when she had a good black-and-white drawing that she was going to add color to, she always practiced first on a few drawings she didn't care about in order to warm up. This writing practice is also a warmup for anything else you might want to write. It is the bottom line, the most primitive, essential beginning of writing. The trust you learn in your own voice can be directed then into a business letter, a novel, a Ph.D. dissertation, a play, a memoir. But it is something you must come back to again and again. Don't think, "I got it! I know how to write. I trust my voice. I'm off to write the great American novel." It's good to go off and write a novel, but don't stop doing writing practice. It is what keeps you in tune, like a dancer who does warmups before dancing or a runner who does stretches before running. Runners don't say, "Oh, I ran yesterday. I'm limber." Each day they warm up and stretch.

Writing practice embraces your whole life and doesn't demand any logical form: no Chapter 19 following the action in Chapter 18. It's a place that you can come to wild and unbridled, mixing the dream of your grandmother's soup with the astounding clouds outside your window. It is undirected and has to do with all of you right in your present moment. Think of writing practice as loving arms you come to illogically and incoherently. It's our wild forest where we gather energy before going to prune our garden, write our fine books and novels. It's a continual practice.

Sit down right now. Give me this moment. Write whatever's running through you. You might start with "this moment" and end up writing about the gardenia you wore at your wedding seven years ago. That's fine. Don't try to control it. Stay present with whatever comes up, and keep your hand moving.

Living Twice

Writers live twice. They go along with their regular life, are as fast as anyone in the grocery store, crossing the street, getting dressed for work in the morning. But there's another part of them that they have been training. The one that lives everything a second time. That sits down and sees their life again and goes over it. Looks at the texture and details.

In a rainstorm, everyone quickly runs down the street with

umbrellas, raincoats, newspapers over their heads. Writers go back outside in the rain with a notebook in front of them and a pen in hand. They look at the puddles, watch them fill, watch the rain splash in them. You can say a writer practices being dumb. Only a dummy would stand out in the rain and watch a puddle. If you're smart, you get in out of the rain so you won't catch cold, and you have health insurance, in case you get sick. If you're dumb, you are more interested in the puddle than in your security and insurance or in getting to work on time.

You're more interested, finally, in living life again in your writing than in making money. Now, let's understand—writers do like money; artists, contrary to popular belief, do like to eat. It's only that money isn't the driving force. I feel very rich when I have time to write and very poor when I get a regular paycheck and no time to work at my real work. Think of it. Employers pay salaries for time. That is the basic commodity that human beings have that is valuable. We exchange our time in life for money. Writers stay with the first step—their time—and feel it is valuable even before they get money for it. They hold on to it and aren't so eager to sell it. It's like inheriting land from your family. It's always been in your family: they have always owned it. Someone comes along and wants to buy it. Writers, if they are smart, won't sell too much of it. They know once it's sold, they might be able to buy a second car, but there will be no place they can go to sit still, no place to dream on.

So it is good to be a little dumb when you want to write. You carry that slow person inside you who needs time; it keeps you from selling it all away. That person will need a place to go and will demand to stare into rain puddles in the rain, usually with no hat on, and to feel the drops on her scalp.

The
Bedquilt

~

BY

DOROTHY CANFIELD

FISHER

O f all the Elwell family Aunt Mehetabel was certainly the most unimportant member. It was in the old-time New England days, when an unmarried woman was an old maid at twenty, at forty was everyone's servant, and at sixty had gone through so much discipline that she could need no more in the next world. Aunt Mehetabel was sixty-eight.

She had never for a moment known the pleasure of being important to anyone. Not that she was useless in her brother's family; she was expected, as a matter of course, to take upon herself the most tedious and uninteresting part of the household labors. On Mondays she accepted as her share the washing of the men's shirts, heavy with sweat and stiff with dirt from the fields and from their own hardworking bodies. Tuesdays she never dreamed of being allowed to iron anything pretty or even interesting, like the baby's white dresses or the fancy aprons of her young lady nieces. She stood all day pressing out a monotonous succession of dish cloths and towels and sheets.

In preserving-time she was allowed to have none of the pleasant responsibility of deciding when the fruit had cooked long enough, nor did she share in the little excitement of pouring the sweet-smelling stuff into stone jars. She sat in a corner with the children and stoned cherries incessantly, or hulled strawberries until her fingers were dyed red.

The Elwells were not consciously unkind to their aunt, they were even in a vague way fond of her; but she was so insignificant a figure in their lives that she was almost invisible to them. Aunt Mehetabel did not resent this treatment; she took it quite as unconsciously as they gave it. It was to be expected when one was an old maid dependent in a busy family. She gathered what crumbs of comfort she could from their occasional careless kindnesses and tried to hide the hurt which even yet pierced her at her brother's rough joking. In the winter when they all sat before the big hearth, roasted apples, drank mulled cider, and teased the girls about their beaux and the boys about their sweethearts, she shrank into a dusky corner with her knitting, happy if the evening passed without her brother saying, with a crude sarcasm, "Ask your Aunt Mehetabel about the beaux that used to come a-sparkin' her!" or, "Mehetabel, how was't when you was in love with Abel Cummings?" As a matter of fact, she had been the same at twenty as at sixty, a mouselike little creature, too shy for anyone to notice, or to raise her eyes for a moment and wish for a life of her own.

Her sister-in-law, a big hearty housewife, who ruled indoors with as autocratic a sway as did her husband on the farm, was rather kind in an absent, offhand way to the shrunken little old woman, and it was through her that Mehetabel was able to enjoy the one pleasure of her life. Even as a girl she had been clever with her needle in the way of patching bedquilts. More than that she could never learn to do. The garments which she made for herself were lamentable affairs, and she was humbly grateful for any help in the bewildering business of putting them together. But in patchwork she enjoyed a tepid importance. She could really do that as well as anyone else. During years of devotion to this one art she had accumulated a considerable store of quilting patterns. Sometimes the neighbors would send over and ask "Miss Mehetabel" for the loan of her sheaf-of-wheat design, or the double-star pattern. It was with an agreeable flutter at being able to help someone that she went to the dresser, in her bare little room under the eaves, and drew out from her crowded portfolio the pattern desired.

She never knew how her great idea came to her. Sometimes she thought she must have dreamed it, sometimes she even wondered reverently, in the phraseology of the weekly prayer meeting, if it had not been "sent" to her. She never admitted to herself that she could have thought of it without other help. It was too great, too ambitious, too lofty a project for her humble mind to have conceived. Even when she finished drawing the design with her own fingers, she gazed at it incredulously, not daring to believe that it could indeed be her handiwork. At first it seemed to her only like a lovely but unreal dream. For a long time she did not once think of putting an actual quilt together following that pattern, even though she herself had invented it. It was not that she feared the prodigious effort that would be needed to get those tiny, oddly shaped pieces of bright-colored material sewed together with the perfection of fine workmanship needed. No, she thought zestfully and eagerly of such endless effort, her heart uplifted by her vision of the mosaic-beauty of the whole creation as she saw it, when she shut her eyes to dream of it—that complicated, splendidly difficult pattern— good enough for the angels in heaven to quilt.

But as she dreamed, her nimble old fingers reached out longingly to turn her dream into reality. She began to think adventurously of trying it out—it would perhaps not be too selfish to make one square— just one unit of her design to see how it would look. She dared do nothing in the household where she was a dependent, without asking permission. With a heart full of hope and fear thumping furiously against her old ribs, she approached the mistress of the house on churning-day, knowing with the innocent guile of a child that the country woman was apt to be in a good temper while working over the fragrant butter in the cool cellar.

Sophia listened absently to her sister-in-law's halting petition. "Why, yes, Mehetabel," she said, leaning far down into the huge churn for the last golden morsels—"why, yes, start another quilt if you want to. I've got a lot of pieces from the spring sewing that will work in real good." Mehetabel tried honestly to make her see that this would be no common quilt, but her limited vocabulary and her emotion stood between her and expression. At last Sophia said, with a kindly impatience: "Oh, there! Don't bother me. I never could keep track of your quiltin' patterns, anyhow. I don't care what pattern you go by."

Mehetabel rushed back up the steep attic stairs to her room, and in a joyful agitation began preparations for the work of her life. Her very first stitches showed her that it was even better than she hoped. By some heaven-sent inspiration she had invented a pattern beyond which no patchwork quilt could go.

She had but little time during the daylight hours filled with the incessant household drudgery. After dark she did not dare to sit up late at night lest she burn too much candle. It was weeks before the little square began to show the pattern. Then Mehetabel was in a fever to finish it. She was too conscientious to shirk even the smallest part of her share of the housework but she rushed through it now so fast that she was panting as she climbed the stairs to her little room.

Every time she opened the door, no matter what weather hung outside the small window, she always saw the little room flooded with sunshine. She smiled to herself as she bent over the innumerable scraps of cotton cloth on her work table. Already—to her—they were arranged in orderly, complex, mosaic-beauty.

Finally she could wait no longer, and one evening ventured to bring her work down beside the fire where the family sat, hoping that good fortune would give her a place near the tallow candles on the mantelpiece. She had reached the last corner of that first square and her needle flew in and out, in and out, with nervous speed. To her relief no one noticed her. By bedtime she had only a few more stitches to add.

As she stood up with the others, the square fell from her trembling old hands and fluttered to the table. Sophia glanced at it carelessly. "Is that the new quilt you said you wanted to start?" she asked, yawning. "Looks like a real pretty pattern. Let's see it."

Up to that moment Mehetabel had labored in the purest spirit of selfless adoration of an ideal. The emotional shock given her by Sophia's cry of admiration as she held the work towards the candle to examine it, was as much astonishment as joy to Mehetabel.

"Land's sakes!" cried her sister-in-law. "Why, Mehetabel Elwell, where did you git that pattern?"

"I made it up," said Mehetabel. She spoke quietly but she was trembling.

"No!" exclaimed Sophia. "Did you! Why, I never did see such a pattern in my life. Girls, come here and see what your Aunt Mehetabel is doing."

The three tall daughters turned back reluctantly from the stairs. "I never could seem to take much interest in patchwork quilts," said one. Already the old-time skill born of early pioneer privation and the craving for beauty, had gone out of style.

"No, nor I neither," answered Sophia. "But a stone image would take an interest in this pattern. Honest, Mehetabel, did you really think of it yourself?" She held it up closer to her eyes and went on, "And how under the sun and stars did you ever git your courage up to start in a-making it? Land! Look at all those tiny squinchy little seams! Why, the wrong side ain't a thing *but* seams! Yet the good side's just like a picture, so smooth you'd think 'twas woven that way. Only nobody could."

The girls looked at it right side, wrong side, and echoed their mother's exclamations. Mr. Elwell himself came over to see what they were discussing. "Well, I declare!" he said, looking at his sister with eyes more approving than she could ever remember. "I don't know a thing about patchwork quilts, but to my eye that beats old Mis' Andrew's quilt that got the blue ribbon so many times at the County Fair."

As she lay that night in her narrow hard bed, too proud, too excited to sleep, Mehetabel's heart swelled and tears of joy ran down from her old eyes.

The next day her sister-in-law astonished her by taking the huge pan of potatoes out of her lap and setting one of the younger children to peeling them. "Don't you want to go on with that quiltin' pattern?" she said. "I'd kind o' like to see how you're goin' to make the grapevine design come out on the corner."

For the first time in her life the dependent old maid contradicted her powerful sister-in-law. Quickly and jealously she said, "It's not a grapevine. It's a sort of curlicue I made up."

"Well, it's nice looking anyhow," said Sophia pacifyingly. "I never could have made it up."

By the end of the summer the family interest had risen so high that Mehetabel was given for herself a little round table in the sitting room, for *her*, where she could keep her pieces and use odd minutes for her work. She almost wept over such kindness and resolved firmly not to take advantage of it. She went on faithfully with her monotonous housework, not neglecting a corner. But the atmosphere of her world was changed. Now things had a meaning. Through the longest task of washing milk-pans, there rose a rainbow of promise. She took her place by the little table and put the thimble on her knotted, hard finger with the solemnity of a priestess performing a rite.

She was even able to bear with some degree of dignity the honor of having the minister and the minister's wife comment admiringly on her great project. The family felt quite proud of Aunt Mehetabel as Minister Bowman had said it was work as fine as any he had ever seen, "and he didn't know but finer!" The remark was repeated verbatim to the neighbors in the following weeks when they dropped in and examined in a perverse Vermontish silence some astonishingly difficult tour de force which Mehetabel had just finished.

The Elwells especially plumed themselves on the slow progress of the quilt. "Mehetabel has been to work on that corner for six weeks, come Tuesday, and she ain't half done yet," they explained to visitors. They fell out of the way of always expecting her to be the one to run on errands, even for the children. "Don't bother your Aunt Mehetabel," Sophia would call. "Can't you see she's got to a ticklish place on the quilt?" The old woman sat straighter in her chair, held up her head. She was a part of the world at last. She joined in the conversation and her remarks were listened to. The children were even told to mind her when she asked them to do some service for her, although this she ventured to do but seldom.

One day some people from the next town, total strangers, drove up to the Elwell house and asked if they could inspect the wonderful quilt which they had heard about even down in their end of the valley. After that Mehetabel's quilt came little by little to be one of the local sights. No visitor to town, whether he knew the Elwells or not, went away without having been to look at it. To make her presentable to strangers, the Elwells saw to it that their aunt was better dressed than she had ever been before. One of the girls made her a pretty little cap to wear on her thin white hair.

A year went by and a quarter of the quilt was finished. A second year passed and half was done. The third year Mehetabel had pneumonia and lay ill for weeks and weeks, horrified by the idea that she might die before her work was completed. A fourth year and one could really see the grandeur of the whole design. In September of the fifth year, the entire family gathered around her to watch eagerly, as Mehetabel quilted the last stitches. The girls held it up by the four corners and they all looked at it in hushed silence.

Then Mr. Elwell cried as one speaking with authority, "By ginger! That's goin' to the County Fair!"

Mehetabel blushed a deep red. She had thought of this herself, but never would have spoken aloud of it.

"Yes indeed!" cried the family. One of the boys was dispatched to the house of a neighbor who was Chairman of the Fair Committee for their village. He came back beaming, "Of course he'll take it. Like's not it may git a prize, he says. But he's got to have it right off because all the things from our town are going tomorrow morning."

Even in her pride Mehetabel felt a pang as the bulky package was carried out of the house. As the days went on she felt lost. For years it had been her one thought. The little round stand had been heaped with a litter of bright-colored scraps. Now it was desolately bare. One of the neighbors who took the long journey to the Fair reported when he came back that the quilt was hung in a good place in a glass case in "Agricultural Hall." But that meant little to Mehetabel's ignorance of everything outside her brother's home. She drooped. The family noticed it. One day Sophia said kindly, "You feel sort o' lost without the quilt, don't you Mehetabel?"

"They took it away so quick!" she said wistfully. "I hadn't hardly had one good look at it myself."

The Fair was to last a fortnight. At the beginning of the second week Mr. Elwell asked his sister how early she could get up in the morning.

"I dunno. Why?" she asked.

"Well, Thomas Ralston has got to drive to West Oldton to see a lawyer. That's four miles beyond the Fair. He says if you can git up so's to leave here at four in the morning he'll drive you to the Fair, leave you there for the day, and bring you back again at night." Mehetabel's face turned very white. Her eyes filled with tears. It was as though someone had offered her a ride in a golden chariot up to the gates of heaven. "Why, you can't *mean* it!" she cried wildly. Her brother laughed. He could not meet her eyes. Even to his easy-going unimaginative indifference to his sister this was a revelation of the narrowness of her life in his home. "Oh, 'tain't so much—just to go to the Fair," he told her in some confusion, and then "Yes, sure I mean it. Go git your things ready, for it's tomorrow morning he wants to start."

A trembling, excited old woman stared all that night at the rafters. She who had never been more than six miles from home—it was to her like going into another world. She who had never seen anything more exciting than a church supper was to see the County Fair. She had never dreamed of doing it. She could not at all imagine what it would be like.

The next morning all the family rose early to see her off. Perhaps her brother had not been the only one to be shocked by her happiness. As she tried to eat her breakfast they called out conflicting advice to her about what to see. Her brother said not to miss inspecting the stock, her nieces said the fancywork was the only thing worth looking at, Sophia told her to be sure to look at the display of preserves. Her nephews asked her to bring home an account of the trotting races.

The buggy drove up to the door, and she was helped in. The family ran to and fro with blankets, woolen tippet, a hot soapstone from the kitchen range. Her wraps were tucked about her. They all stood together and waved goodby as she drove out of the yard. She waved back, but she scarcely saw them. On her return home that evening she was ashy pale, and so stiff that her brother had to lift her out bodily. But her lips were set in a blissful smile. They crowded around her with questions until Sophia pushed them all aside. She told them Aunt Mehetabel was too tired to speak until she had had her supper. The young people held their tongues while she drank her tea, and absent-mindedly ate a scrap of toast with an egg. Then the old woman was helped into an easy chair before the fire. They gathered around her, eager for news of the great world, and Sophia said, "Now, come, Mehetabel, tell us all about it!"

Mehetabel drew a long breath. "It was just perfect!" she said. "Finer even than I thought. They've got it hanging up in the very mid-dle of a sort o' closet made of glass, and one of the lower corners is ripped and turned back so's to show the seams on the wrong side."

"What?" asked Sophia a little blankly.

"Why, the quilt!" said Mehetabel in surprise. "There are a whole lot of other ones in that room, but not one that can hold a candle to it, if I do say it who shouldn't. I heard lots of people say the same thing. You ought to have heard what the women said about that corner, Sophia. They said—well, I'd be ashamed *to tell you* what they said. I declare if I wouldn't!"

Mr. Elwell asked, "What did you think of that big ox we've heard so much about?"

"I didn't look at the stock," returned his sister indifferently. She turned to one of her nieces. "That set of pieces you gave me, Maria, from your red waist, come out just lovely! I heard one woman say you could 'most smell the red roses."

"How did Jed Burgess' bay horse place in the mile trot?" asked Thomas.

"I didn't see the races."

"How about the preserves?" asked Sophia.

"I didn't see the preserves," said Mehetabel calmly.

Seeing that they were gazing at her with astonished faces she went on, to give them a reasonable explanation, "You see I went right to the room where the quilt was, and then I didn't want to leave it. It had been so long since I'd seen it. I had to look at it first real good myself, and then I looked at the others to see if there was any that could come up to it. Then the people begun comin' in and I got so interested in hearin' what they had to say I couldn't think of goin' anywheres else. I ate my lunch right there too, and I'm glad as can be I did, too; for what do you think?"—she gazed about her with kindling eyes. "While I stood there with a sandwich in one hand, didn't the head of the hull concern come in and open the glass door and pin a big bow of blue ribbon right in the middle of the quilt with a label on it, 'First Prize'."

There was a stir of proud congratulation. Then Sophia returned to questioning, "Didn't you go to see anything else?"

"Why, no," said Mehetabel. "Only the quilt. Why should I?"

She fell into a reverie. As if it hung again before her eyes she saw the glory that shone around the creation of her hand and brain. She longed to make her listeners share the golden vision with her. She struggled for words. She fumbled blindly for unknown superlatives. "I tell you it looked like—" she began, and paused.

Vague recollections of hymnbook phrases came into her mind. They were the only kind of poetic expression she knew. But they were dismissed as being sacrilegious to use for something in real life. Also as not being nearly striking enough.

Finally, "I tell you it looked real *good,*" she assured them and sat staring into the fire, on her tired old face the supreme content of an artist who has realized his ideal.

As Busy As We Wanna Be

BY

**DEBORAH
BALDWIN**

~

he gleaming escalators that whisk passengers to and from Washington's high-speed subway never seem to move fast enough for some people. So by unspoken rule, the moving steps have been divided down the middle: On the left is the passing lane. Pause in the passing lane on one of the escalators at, say, the Dupont Circle station, a beehive of white-collar activity ringed by no fewer than five espresso stands, and risk the uncomfortable sensation of some lawyer's briefcase bumping the

back of your knees.

The go-go '80s may be gone, but not the Great American Time Crunch, which is fueled by the perception that there's never enough time to get everything done and, no matter how fast you move, someone—or something—is bound to get there faster. To survive in this caffeinated jungle, we surround ourselves with *objets de temps*—everything from digital watches that beep on the hour to bulging Filofaxes that master our days. We buy computers that measure time in nanoseconds, cars that leap from zero to 60, kitchen equipment able to reduce a head of cabbage to slaw in less time than it takes to clean up afterward.

It may all sound like a losing battle, but here's a little secret from one of the nation's leading experts on time use: With some key exceptions (most notably parents of young children), Americans generally have more free time today than they had 30 years ago—about five hours more a week, to be exact. We're doing less housework, having fewer children, and retiring earlier than previous generations. Many of us are busy, says University of Maryland sociologist John P. Robinson, who heads the Americans' Use of Time Project, *because we want to be.*

Here's another thought: We could return to simpler times. But who would want to?

The fact is, most of us are addicted, as Joni Mitchell once put it, to "the crazies you get from too much choice." As we jump from activity to activity, many of us are also dabbling in a rich stew of opinions, identities, ways of life. Yes, it is possible these days to be a parent, hold down a demanding job, participate in political activities, cultivate an interest in folk art, take up Brazilian cooking, do some traveling, and, in your spare time, carry on a romance with your partner. Or at least it's fun to try.

The busier our schedules, the more important we feel and the easier it is to back out of things we secretly don't want to do, like reading Proust or volunteering at the shelter for the homeless. Yet paradoxically, the more we cram into our lives, the less we feel in control.

My mother likes to refer to a wise and purposeful Catholic saint who, when asked what he would do if he knew he had only a few days left on earth, replied, "Just what I'm doing now."

This radical notion, which implies that one should think about what is important and set about doing it, bears special meaning for those of us who would be more apt to answer, "travel to Bali" or "order everything on the menu at the Four Seasons." What matters in life is not some fantasy of what it would be like to cover a lot of ground and "have" a lot of experiences, as if they could be tagged and stored in a footlocker, but rather the quality of how we choose to live right now.

The problem is not only figuring out what that life might be and how to attain it but also shedding our other possible lives. Thanks in part to the expanding horizons we're exposed to in the media, most of us have a hard time letting go of the multiple fantasies we hold about our future—moving to Paris to join the café society but also knowing the satisfaction of watching seasons change on a Wyoming ranch. Maybe an epiphany one day will lead us to adopt a quiet life that, say, incorporates caring for others while caring for the land—a kind of Wendell Berry meets Dorothy Day vision that will finally pull us away from the distractions of interesting co-workers, new clothes, and cable TV. But until then, we find pleasure in moving through our days as if we were in a supermarket, pulling items from the shelves in a dozen different aisles.

Contrast the sense of everyday well-being expressed by my mother's favorite saint with the barely controlled chaos that characterizes the average two-income household, circa 1994. Rather than rise with the sun and seek transcendence in our herb gardens like medieval monks, we drive to work, put in eight hours, race home, get some exercise, pick up a newspaper, quiz the kids, play the piano, make dinner, take in a movie, turn out for the zoning meeting, learn a second language, write in our journals, squeeze in a few calls to old friends, and pick up a novel before finally passing out.

With so much to choose from, no wonder many of us think we can keep doing a little bit of everything, and somehow the important stuff will take care of itself. And small wonder our powers of concentration are so faint we need written instructions to remember to feed the cat. It was hard to know whether to laugh or applaud when a *Saturday Night Live* send-up advertised an Apple computer that had been crossed with one of those pads of yellow stickums to create the perfect product for today's forgetful, tech-loving consumer: a 3-inch by 3-inch computer notebook that allows users to edit their reminders and stick them to any surface.

We tend to value machines that speed the way, even if they don't ease the load. We're even willing to pay for the opportunity to do two things at once: Witness the rise of cellular phones, audio books, and National Public Radio—which all allow commuters to soak up useful information while they're locked in traffic or stranded at bus stops.

We measure meaning with productivity; maybe that's one reason Americans don't demand more vacation time (we average about half that of Europeans) and speak hopefully about the 12-month school year. It certainly helps explain why professionals who could afford to work fewer hours hesitate to let go of their manic schedules; they fear their co-workers will take them less seriously if they work part time, and maybe take their jobs.

"We're living in a culture of work," says University of Iowa labor historian Benjamin K. Hunnicutt, who co-edits *The Newsletter of the Society for the Reduction of Human Labor.* He bemoans the loss of downtime when people could nurture their heart and soul—"the things we think of as human."

During the early 19th century, the drive was toward fewer

work hours, not more. "Workers adopted the American Revolutionary vision of liberty and applied it to their own lives," Hunnicutt wrote in a 1990 essay. The drive to reduce the number of hours spent on the job ended during the Great Depression, Hunnicutt maintains. In 1932 both political parties endorsed the notion of a 30-hour workweek as a way of spreading jobs around, a reform supported by President Franklin D. Roosevelt until pressure from big business forced him to back down. After that, New Deal programs abandoned shortening the workweek.

More than 50 years later, for the first time in decades, organized labor is once again looking at the possibility of creating jobs by reducing the workweek. "There's no question that the long-term salvation of work lies in reducing working hours," AFL-CIO secretary-treasurer Thomas R. Donahue said. Unfortunately, the cost of health insurance and other benefits compels many employers to do just the opposite, reducing the number of employees and creating more overtime for those who remain on the job.

Whether we're working overtime or punching out early, Americans historically have viewed an active life as morally superior—perhaps one reason so many of us pretend not to like TV. Indeed, writes Cecelia Tichi in her book *Electronic Hearth: Creating an American Television Culture,* a tradition of busy-ness is ingrained in American myth. She points to a series of profiles in Life magazine following World War II that celebrated busy Americans in history. Thomas Jefferson was portrayed as architect, inventor, statesman, and farmer, and Henry David Thoreau, that embodiment of voluntary simplicity, was described as "an industrious writer even at Walden Pond," a man who "may have talked about leisure more than [he] enjoyed it." Women's magazines of the postwar era, in cahoots with the advertising industry, flogged a form of household hyperactivity from women, many of whom had worked during the war but came home to new appliances and the expectation that kitchen floors should be clean enough to eat upon. As Tichi sees it, the powers behind television had to work hard to reconcile America's love affair with busy-ness and the image of pausing in one's round of household duties long enough to watch a soap opera, never mind lolling in a La-Z-Boy with a TV dinner.

The strategy seems to have

worked. Time-use chronicler John Robinson says an astounding 40 percent of the average American's free time dissipates in front of the tube. This may account for some of the discrepancies between Robinson's assertion that we have more free time than a generation ago and most people's feeling that they have less. We may notice less of a chance for reading, visiting, and preparing meals because television absorbs most of our time.

Marked increases in both women working away from home and longer and longer commuting distances also contribute to the feeling that time is running out. Pointing to various trends, including the twin pressures on women to work both at home and away from it, Harvard economist Juliet Schor challenges Robinson's assertion that leisure time is on the rise. Her 1991 best-seller, *The Overworked American: The Unexpected Decline of Leisure*, maintains that Americans are trapped in a work-and-spend cycle with less free time than ever.

And if Robinson believes work hours began to ease up a little bit in the 1960s and '70s, in part because Americans began to use work hours to take care of miscellaneous personal business, Hunnicutt has a different take.

"Instead of viewing progress as a means of transcending work, Americans now view work as an end in itself—the more of it the better," he asserted in his 1990 essay. For some, he believes, it may even have replaced religion.

Part of this is related to cultural traditions that stress independence, perseverance, and hard work, even at the expense of family and neighbors. Ours is a restless nation, constantly in search of the next opportunity. After six years in one house, the average American feels like a hermit crab anxious to shed its shell and move into something new, preferably in a different neighborhood. Hunnicutt also believes America underwent a sea change during the Depression, which instilled the notion that, as he puts it, "there is nothing better than work." Part of the blame, he says, goes not only to politics but also to the collapse of the local community.

For many Americans, the work ethic spills over from job to leisure hours as we set out to achieve results in our "spare" time. This goal-oriented approach to fun is reflected in brisk sales of mile-clocking treadmills and serious sneakers: According to research cited by Witold Rybczynski, author of *Waiting for the Weekend,* in 1989 alone consumers sank more than $13 billion into sports clothing—the equivalent of a billion hours of work. Aside from underscoring the significance we attach to weekend activities, having different costumes for different activities contributes to today's postmodern sensibilities: With each change of clothing—from spandex, which showcases the muscles, to natural fibers, which establish social standing—we can try on something new....

If busy-ness exhausts us, it also fills our multiple lives with multiple purposes. In a quintessentially American way, being busy conveys self-worth, even status. Fitness classes and personal grooming—two major time consumers—complement the great American desire to improve ourselves, and shopping takes care of a powerful urge to consume.

But in talking to pollsters or commenting in diaries kept for Robinson's time-use studies, Americans don't confess a desire to spend more time in the gym, at the mall, or in front of the TV. They say they wish they had more time to socialize with friends and family. A Gallup Poll cited by Juliet Schor found that, when respondents were asked what was most important to them, they ranked family life and betterment of society above "having a nice home, car, and other belongings."

Robinson is probably right in suggesting that what people do is more important than what they say. But sometimes people express a longing long before they act on it. For years, for example, I've been paying lip service to the idea of one day becoming more active in the community, even if it extends only to the end of the block where we live in Washington, D.C., or the public school my daughter attends. But now I find the challenge is to learn new habits, not so easy an undertaking for an office worker with a short attention span and a frontier spirit. It takes some unstructured time, after all, to chat with neighbors in a leisurely way over the back fence. And looking up relatives, in its own way, can be a chore. Plunging into school politics or community organizations means learning to be patient when they eat up valuable time—sometimes in the most inefficient way....

One reason people gravitate toward volunteer work, whether it's tutoring, serving on the PTA, organizing activities at church or school, or working in a soup kitchen, is that it can offer surprising personal rewards, as profound as they are hard to articulate. This is the gist of *The Call of Service: A Witness to Idealism,* a new book by Robert Coles that explores the human need to serve others. Coles doesn't get into the issue of how people value and use their time, although implicit in his life and his work is the notion that there can be no higher calling than donating time to others.

Many of us haven't quite reached that first stage of enlightenment; perhaps we must first pass through a post-'80s period of forsaking materialism for a less tangible, but no less driving, desire to possess time and to wring from it a dozen different experiences—from reading Jane Austen to rafting down the Colorado. Some of this is dilettantism, of course. But it can also reflect a kind of reverence, however perverse, for the fact that we pass this way but once.

Recreation for Special Populations:

A Wheelchair Athlete's Perspective

~

BY

WILLIAM

BOWNESS

magine yourself alone, late at night, driving across a barren
desert. You look up and see a brilliant light falling from the sky.
As you watch, you see the object is not really falling but flying…no
hovering, directly in front of you. You find yourself mesmerized by the
huge oval shape. Staring at the object you can feel yourself being lifted
from your car, not out the door but vaporizing through the steel roof.

Once inside the alien craft you notice that your body hasn't made
the journey. You are inside a different body, an alien body! You can
hear the rhythmic breathing and feel the pulse of this strange shell
that traps you. The shell you now inhabit has arms and legs (at least
that is what they look like) but you can't make anything move! There
you are, the same person that was driving in the desert just moments
earlier, but now entrapped within an alien body.

The above story could have been written in a less sci-fi fashion by
substituting the space craft with an oncoming drunk driver. Instead of
being transported to the alien craft you are taken to the nearest emergency room. Even though your strange body is not an alien form in
appearance it may as well be the Martian body mentioned above. A

doctor informs you that your neck and spinal cord were broken and you won't be able to move anything below your shoulders. There is little chance to reverse the damage.

Just because you are "trapped in a strange body" doesn't mean the "inside you" has changed. Your favorite pizza, baseball team, and TV show are still the same. In fact all of your likes and dislikes remain unchanged. A physical disability does not mean the end of your life. The interests of the disabled are as far-reaching as those of their "able-bodied" peers. Virtually every aspect of recreation and play as found in the able-bodied world is evident in the world of the disabled. There are wheelchair tennis players, water skiers, sky divers, and white water rafting guides. A traumatic injury or disabling disease does not reduce the desire (or need) for competition, high risk, physical challenge, and outdoor adventure. If you liked to snow ski before your injury, chances are you will enjoy the thrill of skiing afterward.

The following is the account of my personal experiences with having a traumatic disabling injury and becoming involved in wheelchair sports. I hope that by sharing a small part of my life, the reader will gain a better insight into the abilities and capabilities of physically challenged people. Further, I hope my story helps people understand just how important recreation is for all people, regardless of their physical or mental limitations.

I can remember the day I went to the Veterans Hospital to visit a friend who had fought in Vietnam. I had once watched him play high school football, and now he was a triple amputee. He was in terrible shape, taking all sorts of pain medication and he barely recognized me when I came in. On my way home I thought to myself that if anything like that happened to me I would not want to live.

This was my first experience with a handicapped individual, and I had no way of knowing it would become a lifelong endeavor for me. Three years later, at the age of eighteen, I was involved in an automobile accident that left me with a broken spinal cord and paralysis from the hips down. There was never a lingering thought about anything except continuing with my life.

Even before the dust settled at the scene of the accident I had a good idea of what had happened to my legs. Having extensive training in emergency first aid I knew I had a spinal injury. At the time I did not really think about the implications this injury would have for the rest of my life. Besides the back injury I also had several broken ribs, which made breathing almost impossible and very painful, internal bleeding, a severed index finger, and several deep cuts on my legs. My immediate concern wasn't whether I would ever walk again but rather if I would make it to see the next day.

I was taken to the nearest hospital and placed in the intensive care unit. One of the doctors called my parents and instructed them to catch the first plane possible because he could not guarantee how long I might live. The first two days after my accident are just a drug-induced dream. I can remember waking up suspended in air, looking at the floor, sandwiched between a rotating "bed" called a Stryker Frame. Every two hours a nurse would turn the frame over and I would go from looking at the floor to looking at the ceiling. After seven days in the intensive care unit I was stable enough to be transported. I was flown via an air ambulance to a large urban hospital in Southern California.

After twenty days of stabilization an operation was performed to fuse my broken vertebra. (The twenty-nine vertebra of the spinal column encase the spinal cord and keep your shoulders from resting on your hips.) Two stainless steel rods called Herrington rods were placed along the broken segment of my back. Bone chips from my pelvis were introduced to start calcification and ultimately fused five vertebrae together. This process was solely to give support to my back, without which I would have been no better off than a jelly fish. The doctors later told me it was apparent that one vertebra had twisted and slipped back, cutting the spinal cord laying directly behind. There would be no hope of any return since they could see where the cord had been cut in two.

The spinal cord is the telephone cable of the human body. It carries messages to and from your brain and all the major organs and extremities in your body. The spinal cord is part of the Central Nervous System (CNS), which consists of the brain, brain stem, and spinal cord. You may have heard about a person who had a finger severed in an accident. The person is rushed to the hospital and the finger is surgically attached. After a brief healing process the finger works just as well as before the accident. The CNS lacks the enzymes that are in the rest of the body that enables nerves to rejoin after they are cut. When there is damage to the spinal cord it usually causes a permanent, irreversible impairment. There is nothing wrong with my brain or legs; simply, the communication between the two has been cut....

At the rehab hospital where I was treated, the physical therapists worked on strength and wheelchair mobility. The occupational therapists taught activities of daily living (ADL). ADLs are such things as getting dressed (try dressing without standing up—it's not impossible, just different), cooking, driving a car, and maneuvering a grocery cart in a crowded store.

The social worker was the liaison between the hospital and my family. She made sure I had a place to go when I was discharged and was helpful filling the gap between me and the real world. The psychologist was there to help lead me through the natural grieving process that follows after a loss. I had lost the use of part of my body and needed to deal with that loss.

Of all the therapies I had contact with, recreational therapy stands alone. When I first arrived at the hospital, "rec" therapy was solely diversional. Table games and an occasional movie were the extent of it. By the time I was discharged I was attending baseball games and day fishing trips and playing basketball at the park across the street.

I had always been an athletic person and the spinal cord injury did not change my desire or need for high risk, competition, and vigorous exercise. While I was still in the hospital I can remember getting my father to take me to the trap and skeet range to shoot. I still had my support jacket and I am sure the doctor would not have seen any humor in this outing. Within weeks of my discharge from the hospital I was on a wheelchair basketball team near my parents' home. I was still the same person I had always been and that lifestyle included the world of athletics.

I enjoyed the profession of recreation so much that I volunteered at the rehab hospital as a recreation aid. Six months later the recreation therapist in the Spinal Cord Unit suddenly left for another position. I was hired as an interim recreation therapist. I worked several months in this position; long enough to decide this was the profession I wanted to pursue. I moved to the small university town of Chico located in Northern California and enrolled in their Recreation Administration program.

I brought with me the knowledge and experience of almost two years of individual and organized team sports. Chico in the late 70s had very little to offer the active disabled individual in the way of organized recreation. Within the year I had together a small core of disabled and able-bodied people to play basketball. That year I was the first wheelchair individual to run in the local marathon. In September of 1980 an energetic Assistant Professor in the Recreation Department and I organized a wheelchair tennis tournament that still continues as an annual event.

Recreation has always been an outlet for me. The tenth anniversary of my auto accident was marked in 1987 and I am doing more in the world of sports than ever before in my life. I am currently the world record holder for sit water skiing in the slalom event (6@35' off at 36 mph) which means I made six buoys behind a 40-foot [12 m] rope with a boat speed of 36 miles [58 km] per hour. I won first place for slalom in the First World Trophy for water skiing held in London, England. I have pushed in over fifteen marathons. (My best time is 2 hours, 28 minutes. The record for the Boston Marathon is 1 hour, 40 minutes!) Before I started water skiing, I was a nationally ranked open-division wheelchair tennis player. I still play for the local basketball team and was chosen for the all-league team in 1986. I have qualified to go to nationals in sit snow skiing and still enjoy snow skiing as a recreational sport. I was a member of (and helped start) the Casa Colina Condors wheelchair basketball team that went on to the Final Four of the National Wheelchair Basketball Association in 1978.

On a recreational level I enjoy hunting, fishing, racquetball, all terrain vehicle (ATV) riding, and camping. I have enjoyed white water rafting, flying, and skin diving. I am currently learning how to fly an ultralight. I honestly believe that I can do anything I set my mind to. I just need to adapt some of the activities to my abilities. However, I must admit that sometimes I get myself in some pretty sticky situations because of this attitude.

For example, one summer I drove from California to Chicago, Illinois, for a tennis tournament. I had loaded my van with all the sports equipment I might need. After the tennis tournament I volunteered at a wheelchair basketball camp that a friend held at the University of Wisconsin, Whitewater. I had brought my marathon chair just in case I might enter a race somewhere along the way. As it turned out the marathon chair came in handy when I went to visit an old friend in Madison just 30 miles [48 km] north.

Madison is a city built on rolling hills around a lake. That evening my friend and I went for what was supposed to be a leisurely jog around her neighborhood. I had broken one of the sacred rules of road racing by not wearing gloves on this push. My marathon chair has no brakes and the only way to stop is to use your hands (that is why gloves are so important).

Whenever we came to the top of a hill I found it easier to speed to the bottom and wait rather than trying to hold my chair back with unprotected hands. This worked well enough until we came to the top of a particularly long, steep hill.

Once more I headed off calling back over my shoulder to my friend that I would see her at the bottom. I thought I heard my running partner call out, "by the way," and thought 'what a strange time to tell me a story.' It was just going to have to wait until she caught up to me. Using the steering device on the front casters of my chair, I was slaloming back and forth across the street trying to control my speed. This worked fine until three cars slowly drove past forcing me to the side of the road and to give up my zig-zag style of speed control.

I began to realize that I was gaining too much speed to be considered under control. To make matters worse, I finally figured out what my friend had tried to tell me at the top. She had not said, "by the way," but "HIGHWAY!" Sure enough, at the bottom of the hill was a six-lane highway full of rush-hour traffic. It was so congested that the cars that had passed me were now backing up at the corner. I tried to brake but the high rate of speed caused a smoky smell to come from my hands. The seriousness of the situation was pointed out by a child looking out the back window of the last car waiting to enter the highway. His face was contorted in a fiendish grin as he pointed out the oncoming runaway to the other occupants of the car.

There was no way I was going to make it across the highway without becoming a spot on the road. I had one last chance to save myself. Once again I reached down to the steering controls and just before passing the car with the child-sadist I turned a hard left. My chair raised up onto the two right wheels and I flew across the street into the driveway of a church (it must have been fate). I became airborne for a couple of seconds, finally ending my flight in a planter of ivy. There I was, still in my chair, sitting in the middle of the ivy. People on the street started applauding as I dusted myself off. I am sure that I am one disabled person that Madison will not soon forget.

I hope my story does not encourage anyone to jump into a track chair without brakes and speed down hills. However, I do hope my personal experiences have helped the reader appreciate that whether in a wheelchair or not, it is up to the individual to make the most of life, and that recreation is a vital component of an exciting, rewarding, and fulfilled existence.

Aides hold Paul Lane's wheelchair as he gets set to throw the discus at track and field meet.

Keeping
Fit

~

BY

NADINE

GORDIMER

reathe.

Breath. A baby, a chicken hatching—the first imperative is to breathe.

Breathless.

Breathe! Out of this concentration, in which he forgets even the rhythm of his feet, is a bellows pumped by the command, the admonition, the slap on the bottom that shocks the baby into inhalation—comes his second wind. Unless you go out like this, morning and evening, you never know what no one can remember, that first discovery of independent life: I can breathe.

It came after twenty minutes or so, when he had left behind houses he had never entered but knew because they were occupied by people like himself, passed the aggressive monitoring of dogs who were at their customary gateposts, the shuttered take-away, *prego rolls & jumbo burgers,* and the bristling security cage of the electricity substation. These were his pedometer: three kilometres. Here where the grid of his familiar streets came up short against the main road was the point of no return. Sometimes he took a circuitous route back but this was the outward limit. Not quite a highway, the road divided the territory of Alicewood, named for the daughter of a real estate developer, from Enterprise Park, the landscaped industrial buffer between the suburb and the black township whose identity was long overwhelmed by a squatter camp which had spread to the boundary of the industries and, where there was vacant ground, dragged through these interstices its detritus of tin and sacking, abutting on the highway. Someone—the municipality—had put up a high corrugated metal fence to shield passing traffic from the sight.

At six o'clock on a Sunday morning the four-lane road is deserted. A wavering of smoke from last night's cooking fires hangs peacefully, away on the other side, the sign of existence there. In the house he has left, a woman, three children, sleep on unaware that he has risen from her bed, passed their doors, as if he has left his body in its shape impressed beside her and moved out of himself on silent running shoes. The exhausted tarmac gives off a bitumen scent that is lost in carbon monoxide fumes during the week; he is quietly attracted, at his turning point, to mark time a few paces out on the road, having the pounded surface all to himself. It is pleasant as a worn rubber mat underfoot.

He began to run steadily along it. Now no landmarks of distance; instead, memory in a twin stream started to flow in its own progression, the pumping of his heart sending blood to open up where in his brain cells flashes of feeling and images from boyhood were stored at one with the play of fragments from the past week. Tadpoles wriggling in his pocket on his way home from school and the expression of irritation round his accountant's mouth when he disputed some calculation, the change in the curve of a girl's buttocks as she shifted her weight from one leg to another standing in front of him in a bank queue on Friday and the sudden surfacing of his father's figure bending about in a vegetable garden, looming, seen at the height of a child who has done wrong (run away, was it?); the same figure and not the same, with an arthritic leg laid out like a wooden one and the abstracted glance of someone able now only to move towards death, the scent of the girl in the bank as her sharp exhalation of impatience sent the message of her body to his—all this smoothly breathed, in and out. In the flowing together of contexts the crow of a cock in the city does not come incongruously but is more of a heraldic announcement: day, today, time for ghosts to fade, time to return. The cock-crow sounds from over there behind the fence, a place which itself has come about defying context, plan, definition, confusing the peasant's farmyard awakening with the labourer's clock-in at the industries close by.

Of course, they kept chickens among whatever dirt and degradation was behind that fence. He must have done another couple of kilometres;

there were no more factory buildings but the shanties occupied the land all along the other side of the road. Here in places the metal fence had collapsed under the pressure of shelters that leant against it and sections had been filched to roof other shacks, yet the life in there was not exposed to the road because the jumbled crowding of makeshift board and planks, bits of wrecked vehicles, cardboard and plastic sheeting closed off from view how far back the swarm of habitation extended. But as he turned to go home—it burst open, revealing itself.

Men came flying at him. The assault exaggerated their faces like close-ups in film; for a vivid second he saw rather than felt through the rictus of his mouth and cheek muscles the instant gaping fear that must have opened his mouth and stretched his cheeks like a rubber mask. They rushed over him colliding with him, swerving against him, battering him. But in their passage: they were carrying him along with them. They were not after him. Fuses were blowing in the panic impulses along the paths of his brain, he received incoherently the realization that he was something in their path—a box they tripped over, an abandoned tyretube bowling as they kicked past it—swept into their pursuit. What had seemed to be one of them was the man they were after, and that man's terror and their rage were a single fury in which he hadn't distinguished one from the other. The man's shirt was ripped down the back, another hobbled wildly with one shoe lost, some wore red rags tied pirate-style round their heads, knobbed clubs swung above them, long pieces of wire strong and sharp enough to skewer a man armed them, one loped with a sledge-hammer over his shoulder, there were cleavers, and a butcher's knife ground to sword-point and dangling from a bracelet of plaited red plastic. They were bellowing in a language he didn't need to understand in order to understand, the stink of adrenaline sweat was coming from the furnace within them. The victim's knees pumped up almost to his chin, he zigzagged about the road, the road that was never to be crossed, and the tight mob raced with him, hampered and terrible with their weaponry, and he who had blundered into the chase was whirled along as if caught up by some carnival crowd in which, this time, the presence of death was not fancy dress.

The race of pursued and pursuers broke suddenly from one side of the road to the other, he was thrust to the edge of the wild press and saw his chance.

Out.

The fence was down. The squatter shacks: he was on the wrong side. The road was no longer the sure boundary between that place and his suburb. It was the barrier that prevented him from getting away from the wrong side. In the empty road *(would no one come, would no one stop it)* the man went down under chants and the blows of a club with a gnarled knob as big as a child's head, the butcher's knife plunged, the pointed wires dug, the body writhed away like a chopped worm. On the oil stains of the tarmac blood was superimposing another spill.

He fled down among the shacks. Two bare-arsed children squatting to pee jumped up and bounded from him like rats. A man lifted the sack over an aperture in tin and quickly let it fall. There were cooking pots and ashes and a tethered donkey, the scabby body of a car like the eviscerated shell of a giant beetle, lamed supermarket trolleys, mud walls, beer cans; silence. Desertion; or the vacuum created by people left behind by the passage of violence, keeping out of it, holding breath. The haphazard strips of muddy passage between whatever passed for walls were so narrow he seemed to have entered a single habitation where, unseen, people all around followed him—his breathing, his panting breath—from room to room. A white man! he felt himself only to be a white man, no other identity, no other way to be known: to pull aside a sack and say, I'm in brokerage, give his name, his bona fide address—that was nothing, these qualifications of his existence meant nothing. And then a woman appeared out of a shack that had a door.— Get inside. It's dangerous.—A firm grip, a big butterscotch-coloured upper arm in a tight-filled short sleeve, yellow- and pink-flowered. He ducked into her doorway with a push from her in his back.

—They terrible, those people, they'll kill anybody. They will.—She had the strict face formed by respectability, a black woman churchgoer's face, her eyes distant and narrowed behind butterfly-shaped spectacle frames with gilt scrolls. Other people in dimness were staring. A piece of canvas hung over what must be a square of window. Light came only from the gaps between tin walls and the roof low on his head.—You see, I run... I was just on the other side of the road, out for a run...—

A young man who was turned away from this apparition, paring his nails, children, a stooping man in pyjama trousers and a pullover, a girl with a blanket wrapped round her body below naked shoulders, *doek* awry from sleep.

He had a momentary loss of control, wanting to collapse against the woman, clutch her used big body under her apron and take the shield of her warmth against his trembling.—What's happening—who was it—he's dead there, in the road.—

She spoke for everyone.—From the hostel. They come from the hostel, they come in here and kill us.—

—I read about it.—His head wagged like a puppet's, down, down to his chest.

—You read about it!—She gave a short slap of a laugh. —Every night, we don't know. They come or they don't come—

—Who are they?—

—The police send them.—

He could not say to this woman, That's not what I read.

—Tomorrow it can be *him*.—The woman uncrossed her fine arms and presented the profile of the young man.

—Him?—

—Yes, my son. Come and knock on the wall shouting it's all right, call him comrade so he'll believe, and if he doesn't go out, break in and beat my husband, there, you see him, he's an old man already—take my son and kill him.—

Nothing moves a man on behalf of others so surely as danger to himself.—It was wonderful of you to open your door like that. I mean, for me. I don't know what to say. Why him? What would make them come for your son?—

The young man shifted abruptly, turning still more pointedly away from the apparition his mother had brought in among them.

—My son's in the Youth—the street committee.—

The kind who burned government appointees' houses, stoned buses, boycotted schools. And lived here—slowly he was making out of the dimness and his own shock what this habitation was. Its intimacy pressed around him, a mould in which his own dimensions were redefined. He took up space where the space allowed each resident must be scrupulously confined and observed. The space itself was divided in two by curtains which stretched across it, not quite drawn closed, so that he could see the double bed with a flounced green satin cover which filled one half. A table with pots and a spirit stove, a dresser with crockery, a sagging armchair into which the old man sank, a chromium-shiny radio cassette player, a girlie calendar, Good Shepherd Jesus, framed, with a gold tinsel halo, the droop of clothes hanging from nails, vague darkness of folded blankets—that was the second half. He saw now there were three children as well as the grown daughter and son; seven people lived here.

The woman had lit the spirit stove and she gave an order, in their language, to the girl. Holding the blanket in one hand and shuffling with her knees together in modesty, the girl fetched a cup and saucer from the dresser, wiped them with a rag, put a spoon of powdered milk in the cup and, chivvied again by her mother, a spoon of tea in a jug. Like a sleep-walker. No one spoke except the woman. But he felt their awareness of him: the old man bewildered as at a visitor he hadn't been told to expect, the children in unblinking curiosity, the young man hostile, the girl—the girl wanting to sink through the earth that was the shack's floor; as if *he* were the threat, and not the marauders whose gales of anger blew about from the road, rising and fading as a wind would gust against the tin walls. The old man suddenly got up and signalled him to take the armchair.

—Please stay where you are, I don't need—

The woman brought him the cup of tea, carrying a small tin of sugar.—No, no, sit, sit. You see what this place is like, the rain pours in, you see how we have to try and stuff around the tin with plastic, but we can still greet with a chair.—

While he drank the paraffin-tasting tea she stood above him admonishingly.—You must keep away from here.—

—I don't usually come so far, it was just only this morning, and I was right on the other side of the main road, there was no one... it happened, I got in the way.—

She pinched her lips between her teeth and shook her head at fool-ishness.—What do you want to come near this place for.—

Don't take any chances keep away from the main road— his wife, when he ran sometimes before going to bed at night, possessive, not wanting him to do anything that excluded her.

—I can rather go to my home there in Lebowa, but how can we go, he's got a job in town, he's the attendant at underground parking, you'll see him there by the chain where the cars come in to go down under the building. He's too old to stay here now alone.—

The baying from the road swerved away out of hearing. Morning sounds, of coughing, wailing babies, and the drumming of water on tin containers, were released. He stood up and put the cup down carefully on the table.

—Wait.—She turned and said something to the young man. He answered with the smouldering obstinacy of adolescence. She spoke once more, and he put his head out of the door. All held the exact posi-tion in which the narrow stream of morning sunlight found them; the boy slipped out and closed them into dimness behind him. The woman did not speak while he was away. Darkness danced with the after-vision of the boy's profile against glare; the waiting was the first atmosphere shared with the one to whom refuge had been given. He could hear them breathing as he breathed.

The son came back surly and said nothing. His mother went up to challenge him face to face. And he answered in monosyllables she drew from him.

—It's all right now. But you like to run, so run.—He felt she was teasing him, in the relief of tension. But she would not presume to laugh with a white man, her matronly dignity was remote as ever.

He shook hands with the old man, thanking him, thanking them all, awkwardly, effusively—no response, as he included the children, the son and daughter—hearing his own voice as if he were talking to himself.

He opened the door. With crossed arms, she contemplated him.— God bless you.—

The telling of it welled up in his mouth like saliva; he was on the right side, running home to tell what had happened to him. He swallowed and swallowed in urgency, unable to get there fast enough. Now and then his head tossed as he ran; in disbelief. All so quick. A good pace, quiet and even on the soft tarmac, not a soul in sight, and before you have the time to take breath—to prepare, to decide what to do—it happens. Suddenly, this was sensational. That's how it will happen, always happens everywhere! Keep away. They came over, at him, not after him, no, but making him join them. At first he didn't know it, but he was racing with them after blood, after the one who was to lie dying in the road. That's what it really means to be caught up, not to know what you are doing, not to be able to stop, say no!—that awful unimagined state that has been with you all the time. And he had nothing to give the woman, the old man; when he ran, he kept on him only a few silver coins along with his house key in the minute pocket which, like the cushioned pump action of their soles, was a feature of his shoes. Could hardly tip her coins. But if he went back, another time, with say, a hundred rands, fifty rands, would he ever find the shack among so many? Should have asked her where she worked, obviously she must be a domestic or something like that, so that he could have rewarded her properly, found her at her place of employment. Where was it the husband held one of those chains you see before the ramp of a firm's underground car park? Had she named the street? How shit-scared he must have been (he jeered) not to take in properly what the woman said! She probably saved his life; he felt the euphoria of survival. It lasted through the pacing of half a block. A car with men in golf caps, going to tee off early, passed him, and several joggers, just up, approached and went by with a comradely lift of the hand; he felt that his experience must blaze in his face if only they had known how to look, if only they had learnt.

But don't exaggerate.

Had his life really been in danger? He could have been killed by a blow to get him out of the way, yes, that sledgehammer—it might have struck a glancing blow. The butcher's knife, cleaver, whatever the horrible thing was with its sword-point and that woven bracelet like the pretty mats they make and sell on the streets, it could scalp you, open your throat with one swing. But they didn't even seem to see him. They saw only the one they were after, and it wasn't him. Under the rise and fall of his feet on the grassy suburban pavement blood drew its pattern on tarmac.

Who knew whether she was telling the truth when she said it was the police who sent them to make trouble?

He read the papers, for all he knew it could have been Inkatha murdering someone from the ANC, it could have been people from the street committees she said the boy belonged to, out to get a local councillor regarded as a government stooge, it could have been ANC people avenging themselves on a police informer. He didn't know how to read the signs of their particular cause as someone like her would from the rags they had tied round their heads or the kind of weapons they'd improvised for themselves, the cries they chanted. He had to believe her, whatever she'd chosen to tell him. Whatever side she was on—god knows, did she know herself, shut in that hovel, trying to stay alive—she had opened her door and taken him in.

Why?

Why should she have?

God bless you.

Out of Christian caritas? Love—that variety? But he was not welcome in the hovel, she had kept the distaste, the resentment, the unease at his invasion at bay, but herself had little time for his foolish blundering. *What do you want to come near this place for.* He heard something else: *Is there nowhere you think you can't go, does even this rubbish dump belong to you if you need to come hiding here, saving your skin.* And he had shamefully wanted to fling himself upon her, safe, safe, reassured, hidden from the sound and sight of blows and blood as he could be only by one who belonged to the people who produced the murderers and was not a murderer.

As he came level with the security cage of the electricity sub-station, the take-away, and then the garage and the houses prefiguring his own, the need to tell began to subside inside him with the slowing of his heartbeat. He heard himself describing his amazement, his shock, even (disarmingly honest confession) his shit-scaredness, enjoying the tears (dread of loss) in the eyes of his wife, recounting the humble goodness of the unknown woman who had put out her round butterscotch-coloured arm and pulled him from danger, heard himself describing the crowded deprivation of the shack where too few possessions were too many for it to hold, the bed curtained for some attempt at the altar of privacy; the piously sentimental conclusion of the blessing, as he was restored to come home for breakfast. The urge to tell buried itself where no one could get it out of him because he would never understand how to tell; how to get it all straight.

—A bit excessive, isn't it? Exhausting yourself—His wife was half-reproachful, half-amused at the sight of shining runnels on his face and his mouth parted the better to breathe. But she was trailing her dressing-gown, barefoot, only just out of bed and she certainly had no idea how early he had left or how long he had been absent while the house slept. Over her cereal his daughter was murmuring to a paper doll in one of the imaginary exchanges of childhood, he could hear the boys racing about in the garden; each day without fingerprints, for them.

He drank a glass of juice, and another, of water.—I'll eat later.—

—I should think so! Go and lie down for a while. Are you trying to give yourself a heart attack? What kind of marathon is this. How far have you been today, anyway?—

—I don't keep track.—

—Yes, that's evident, my darling! You don't.—

In the bedroom the exercise bicycle, going nowhere.

In brokerage, her darling, resident at this address. He took off his running shoes and threw his shirt on the carpet. He stank of the same sweat as those he was caught up among within a pursuit he did not understand.

The unmade bed was blissful. Her lilac-patterned blue silk curtains were still drawn shut but the windows were open and the cloth undulated with a breeze that touched his moist breast-hair with a light hand. He closed his eyes. Some extremely faint, high-pitched, minute sound made timid entry at the edge of darkness; he rubbed his ear, but it did not cease. Longing to sleep, he tried to let the sound sink away into the tide of his blood, his breath. If he opened his eyes and was distracted by the impressions of the room—the dressing-table with the painted porcelain hand where her necklaces and ear-rings hung, the open wardrobe with his ties dangling thick on a rack, a red rose tripled in the angle of mirrors, his briefcase abandoned for the weekend on the chaise-longue, the exercise bicycle—he heard the sound only by strain-ing to. But the moment he was in darkness it was there again: plaintive, feeble, finger-nail scratch of sound. He staggered up and went slowly about the room in search of the source like a blind man relying on one sense alone. It was behind a wall somewhere, penetrating the closed space of his head from some other closed space. A bird. A trapped bird. He narrowed the source; the cheeping came from a drain-pipe outside the window.

His bare feet slapping flat-footed with fatigue, he slumped back to the breakfast table.—There's a bird trapped in the drain-pipe outside the bedroom.—

—So the kids told me.—

—Well let them take the ladder and get it out.—

—It must be a chick from the nest those mynahs built under the eaves. Fell into the gutter and then down the pipe, so it's stuck—what can the boys do?—

—So what's to be done about it?—

—Can't exactly call the fire brigade. Poor little thing. Just wait for it to die.—

Back in the room, on the bed, he listened. Eyes closed. Every time the sound paused he had to wait for it to begin again. Die. It would not die. In another darkness the most insignificant of fragments of life cried out, kept crying out. He jumped from the bed and burst through the house, going after her, bellowing, his hands palsied with rage.— Get the bloody thing out, can't you! Push up a pole, take the ladder, pull down the drain-pipe, for Christ' sake!—

She stared at him, distancing herself from this exhibition.

—What do you expect of little boys? I won't have them break their necks. Do it then! *You* do it. Do it if you can. You're so athletic.—

In the Dove-Grey Dove-Soft Dusk

BY
DENNIS
BRUTUS

In the dove-grey, dove-soft dusk
when the walls softened to frozen smoke
and their rigidity melted
receding to miles,
when the air was alive and tender
with a mist of spray from the sea,
the air luminous
and the sky bright with the dulling glimmer
of cooling molten lead;
when the island breathed—
trees, grass, stones and sand breathing
quietly at the end of the long hot day—
and the sea was a soft circling presence—
no longer a tight barbed menacing ring:
in the dusk
nothing was more agonizing than to be seized
by the poignant urgent simple desire
simply to stroll in the quiet dusk:
as I do now:
as I do now, and they do not.

A
Walker's
Manual

~

BY

BETTE

PESETSKY

Whenever possible, I walk to my destination. In order to do this, I must live at the very center of my activities. I am not referring to walking as chore or as exercise but rather as function, which, like breathing or drinking, cannot be stopped. By constant walking, I have learned to use my hips and to extend the length of my stride. Although I seem to be a fast walker to those who move no more than from taxi to building, I wear no speedometer and neither run nor jog. When it rains, I ride, and I would never think of carrying heavy things in my arms. In other words, I am not an obsessive walker, just a very good one.

I feel sorry for those who do not walk and thus see the world only from start to finish. Once, I joined a walking club and rambled in the countryside. But the other walkers made too much of it. They spoke of measured distances and of time, and when they walked, it was a formal activity. They wagered on endurance.

My only concession to scheduling is to map out my daily rounds. It is inefficient to do otherwise. On the back of my kitchen door I have pinned a map with a red dot to represent my apartment house. Cross-streets for forty blocks in any direction are indicated. In ink, I have noted all the places where I might stop. Stores, theaters, homes of friends—a useful navigational scheme.

While walking, you have truly a chance to see. That is the pleasure of walking. The fifteenth-century monk Hegastus, who set himself walking as a penance, was horrified to discover how much he enjoyed the physical movement, how stimulating was the passing scene, men in fields, children at play. He prayed for guidance as his soles wore thin. He sent back letters intended for a pamphlet on the torment of walking. At last he bought shoes made by a poor craftsman. Calluses and bunions appeared. In bleeding pain and joy, he returned to the monastery.

My paternal grandmother, an Eastern European lady in whose custody I was often left, feared the intricacies of buses and subways. If you missed your stop on the subway, God knew where you would land. Once, holding tight to my hand, she took me on a subway. We were going in search of a freshly killed chicken in a store that might or might not be mythical. We missed our station, and when we ventured up the stairs to the street, it was to stand in an area of warehouses. As my grandmother muttered a prayer for our salvation, a car stopped across the street, and two men got out. One shot the other. The dead man fell face down. This is what happens when you don't know where you're going.

My daughter Danielle does not walk, although she has hiked the Appalachian Trail and marched down into the Grand Canyon. She was the first in her group to have black patent slippers with T-straps. You cannot walk in such shoes. For children, it is best to buy brown leather oxfords, snub-nosed with a well-sewn heel. Christina of Sweden, in her romantic journey through New England, gave up pinching slippers for moccasins made of calfskin. A yielding shoe is the first necessity. A moccasin with padded sole provided Christina of Sweden with the perfect footwear to move through the forest and along unpaved streets.

Walking leads to many pleasures. One afternoon in the suburbs, Georgette ran from her house and stood in the road wringing her hands. She offered me fifty dollars a week for life if I would never speak of the car that pulled into her driveway every afternoon at three. Of course, I took the money.

When you walk down a street, you look in windows, even into the windows of apartments or private residences if the blinds are up or the drapes are open. It was a miniature Queen Anne desk in the window of an antique store that caught my attention, and I stopped. It was then that I saw them walking across the street. I had never seen her before.

She was young already, as I knew, early twenties, I'd say, slender and small and not unpretty. Her head just reached his shoulder. They weren't holding hands, but their arms swung together in an intimate rhythm. Occasionally their fingers clasped and unclasped. She wore a plaid coat and a small red tam. Rigidly, I faced the store window, grateful that the street was wide. I followed their disgusting progress in the reflections of glass. She walked at a pace presumably not naturally hers—this, I surmised, to keep up with him. Two short steps and then a little skip. She was what Danielle would call smart, stylish. She looked okay to me too.

I started forward, foolishly quickening my step until I felt the beat of my heart. It was inevitable that I should at some time or other see my former husband. No matter what else changes, habits remain—the same bakery, tailor, dimestore. Charmel, in his account of walking through England, speaks of meeting the same person first down one twist of the road and then again far away on another. Charmel, as best I can recall, does not mention his opinion of the people he thus encountered. My former husband, whom I have not seen for five years, a period long enough for wariness to dissolve, is not, however, someone I hold in high regard. We last met in the lawyer's office, divvying up the spoils.

I forced myself to complete my chores. I stopped in at the cleaners, where they were altering a skirt for me. Midcalf with a single pleat in the front. Too much material in a garment causes it to flap about the knees. It is tiring and interferes with movement. Slacks, of course, are perfect. They permit the stride unfettered. But skirts are once again in fashion and, being single, so must be I.

I carry paper bags in one hand and the box with the skirt in the other. Nigel said that the best time he had was strolling through Paris carrying nothing and buying nothing, a single key and two coins in his pocket.

～

The search for the perfect boot is difficult. It must protect the foot from the cold, yet remain light and supple. The boots that I already own are unsatisfactory. First of all, there is the question of appearance;

those boots are thick and unshapely, suitable for suburban snowbanks. Friends tell me of a mail-order bootmaker in Maine, fearsomely expensive. I take the measurements that his advertisement requests and attach these to a cardboard tracing of my feet. The boots, ordered late, do not arrive until early December. When I open the package, the things within tremble. The leather softened with neat's-foot oil glows and glistens with life. I am transformed. The dreariness of winter is lifted.

I go forth again, my stride never better than it is. It is past two in the afternoon, and I am almost late for my two-twenty class in antiques. The school is twelve blocks away. After class, I stop in the midtown library for the books that I have reserved on dolls. In his heuristic account *Winter Walks,* LeGere says that in the wind one must remove one's head-covering and permit the hair to blow freely. The pleasure will make the cold as nothing. As I unfastened my scarf, they emerged from a restaurant hardly more than a cold breath away. He holds her arm as he escorts her to the edge of the curb. Then he turns up his collar against the weather and steps into the street to signal for a cab. She waits on the sidewalk, secure and confident. One thing he never had with me was trouble getting a taxi.

I was paralyzed. Nothing could have made my legs move past them. A taxi did a pas de deux through the traffic and slid to the curb. He opened the door and stood back for her to enter. She wore high boots made for curb-to-building travel. His hand touched her arm. I take care of you, the gesture said.

Following Danielle's advice, I have my hair cut. It will be a while before I can adjust. Gusts no longer whip stray strands across my forehead as I walk. I have the giddy sensation of false Ménière's disease. As a child, I read an interview with the ingenue Sally Martin. She said that after her hair was bobbed she walked through the streets with the first liberty she had known in years.

Jake, a friend from college days, is giving a party at his Long Island estate. The waterfront paths permit one to walk for two unobstructed miles. I planned to go. Mr. Stanley would be my escort. I'd met him at an auction, where he bought a small wooden train and a doll I didn't want. Afterwards, we talked. I found him amusing and companionable enough. I bought a silver-gray chiffon dress, the merest froth of a garment, dips and panels and triangular sleeves. There are occasions, perhaps once or twice in your life, when you look extremely right, and the narcissistic impulse races forward. I caught glimpses of myself in every reflective object.

So I walked with Mr. Stanley through the summer night. Mr. Stanley was chilled. We returned to the house. As we sipped champagne in the second-floor ballroom, I saw them enter the hall. I was truly startled. Jake must know her. That must be it. I turned away, wondering if I dared suggest to my escort that we tour the grounds again. Her hair, as long as Danielle's, swung free. She wore silk pajamas with the color, the cut, the swagger of youth.

I decided that she looked unutterably out of place.

My attention turned to my foot. It hurt. It was the silver sandal, a concession to the dress. The next morning I could barely hobble. I went to my podiatrist. "Stay off your feet," he said.

I have decided to have all my footwear made by hand. I begin to think about the last, about the instep, about interior construction and ventilation. These feet of mine must serve me till the end. On both sides of my family the women lived well into their eighties. The daughter of the King of Seville practically walked to her funeral.

I am walking down the west side of the street to avoid the direct heat of the sun. I see them waiting across the way for the light to change.

I have placed the key to my apartment on a chain around my neck and I have wrapped in tissue three one-dollar bills tucked into the single pocket of my cotton skirt. I have abandoned all synthetic materials for the summer. Pure cotton absorbs perspiration and keeps the body cool. Unfortunately, I am sometimes recognized by residents and shopkeepers on certain streets. But I do not break my stride. I pretend to be winding my watch. Or I clutch my jaw in imaginary pain. People, the eighteenth-century philosopher Langer writes, do not understand an activity that is beyond their understanding.

The Trout Pond

BY

MILTON ACORN

for R.F. Acorn 1897-1968

The woods, spruce twisted
into spooky shapes
echo the trickle of water
from raised oars.

Above the pale ripples
a redwing blackbird fastens,
legs crooked and beak alert,
to a springing reed.

My father's whiteheaded now,
but oars whose tug
used to start my tendons
pull easily these years.

His line curls, his troutfly drops
as if on its own wings,
marks a vee on the mirrored
ragged spruceheads, and
a crane flapping past clouds.

After Apple-Picking

BY

ROBERT

FROST

My long two-pointed ladder's sticking through a tree
Toward heaven still,
And there's a barrel that I didn't fill
Beside it, and there may be two or three
Apples I didn't pick upon some bough.
But I am done with apple-picking now.
Essence of winter sleep is on the night,
The scent of apples: I am drowsing off.
I cannot rub the strangeness from my sight
I got from looking through a pane of glass
I skimmed this morning from the drinking trough
And held against the world of hoary grass.
It melted, and I let it fall and break.
But I was well
Upon my way to sleep before it fell,
And I could tell
What form my dreaming was about to take.
Magnified apples appear and disappear,
Stem end and blossom end,
And every fleck of russet showing clear.

My instep arch not only keeps the ache,
It keeps the pressure of a ladder-round.
I feel the ladder sway as the boughs bend.
And I keep hearing from the cellar bin
The rumbling sound
Of load on load of apples coming in.
For I have had too much
Of apple-picking: I am overtired
Of the great harvest I myself desired.
There were ten thousand thousand fruit to touch,
Cherish in hand, lift down, and not let fall.
For all
That struck the earth,
No matter if not bruised or spiked with stubble,
Went surely to the cider-apple heap
As of no worth.
One can see what will trouble
This sleep of mine, whatever sleep it is.
Were he not gone,
The woodchuck could say whether it's like his
Long sleep, as I describe its coming on,
Or just some human sleep.

Tired

~

BY

SHEL

SILVERSTEIN

I've been working so hard you just wouldn't believe,
And I'm tired!
There's so little time and so much to achieve,
And I'm tired!
I've been lying here holding the grass in its place,
Pressing a leaf with the side of my face,
Tasting the apples to see if they're sweet,
Counting the toes on a centipede's feet.
I've been memorizing the shape of that cloud,
Warning the robins to not chirp so loud,
Shooing the butterflies off the tomatoes,
Keeping an eye out for floods and tornadoes.
I've been supervising the work of the ants
And thinking of pruning the cantaloupe plants,
Timing the sun to see what time it sets,
Calling the fish to swim into my nets,
And I've taken twelve thousand and forty-one breaths,
And I'm TIRED!

To Be of Use

BY

MARGE

PIERCY

The people I love the best
jump into work head first
without dallying in the shallows
and swim off with sure strokes almost out of sight.
They seem to become natives of that element,
the black sleek heads of seals
bouncing like half-submerged balls.

I love people who harness themselves, an ox to a heavy cart,
who pull like water buffalo, with massive patience,
who strain in the mud and the muck to move things forward,
who do what has to be done, again and again.

I want to be with people who submerge
in the task, who go into the fields to harvest
and work in a row and pass the bags along,
who stand in the line and haul in their places,
who are not parlor generals and field deserters
but move in a common rhythm
when the food must come in or the fire be put out.

The work of the world is common as mud......
Botched, it smears the hands, crumbles to dust.
But the thing worth doing well done
has a shape that satisfies, clean and evident.
Greek amphoras for wine or oil,
Hopi vases that held corn, are put in museums
but you know they were made to be used.

ACKNOWLEDGEMENTS

Care has been taken to trace ownership of copyright material contained in this text. The publishers will gladly accept any information that will enable them to rectify any reference or credit in subsequent editions.

TEXT

p. 4 "The Problem of Leisure" by Witold Rybczynski. From *Waiting for the Weekend* by Witold Rybczynski. Copyright © Witold Rybczynski, 1991. Reprinted by permission of Penguin Books Canada Limited; **p. 10** "A New Vision of Livelihood" by Matthew Fox. Matthew Fox, a former Catholic and now an Episcopal priest, is the director of the Institute in Culture and Creation Spirituality at Holy Names College in Oakland, CA. He is the author of sixteen books including *The Reinvention of Work* (HarperCollins); **p. 13** "Picking Potatoes" by David Weale. Reprinted from *Them Times* by David Weale (Charlottetown: Institute of Island Studies, 1992), by permission of the author; **p. 16** "I Liked to Shuck Peas" by John B. Lee. Appeared in John B. Lee's book *These Are the Days of Dogs and Horses*, Black Moss Press, 1994. Reprinted by permission of the author and publisher; **p. 18** "Dirty Work" by Robert Fulghum. From *It Was on Fire When I Lay Down on It* by Robert Fulghum. Copyright © 1988, 1989 by Robert Fulghum. Reprinted by permission of Random House, Inc.; **p. 22** "heritage" by Anita Skeen. Reprinted by permission of the author; **p. 24** "Hades" by Robert Hilles. This story will also be appearing in *Near Morning* published by Black Moss Press, Fall, 1995. Reprinted by permission of Robert Hilles; **p. 26** "Fern Hill" by Dylan Thomas. From *Collected Poems 1934-1952* by Dylan Thomas, published by J. M. Dent & Sons Ltd., 1966. Reprinted by permission of David Higham Associates; **p. 28** From *Wordstruck* by Robert MacNeil. Copyright © 1989 by Neely Productions, Ltd. Used by permission of Viking Penguin, a division of Penguin Books USA Inc.; **p. 31** "The Playground" by Ray Bradbury. Reprinted by permission of Don Congdon Associates, Inc. Copyright © 1953, renewed 1981 by Ray Bradbury; **p. 46** "Part-time Work: Challenge or Handicap in High School?" by Allen Panzeri. Reprinted by permission of *The Edmonton Journal*; **p. 49** "Child Workers Risking Death" by Leslie Papp. Reprinted with permission – The Toronto Star Syndicate; **p. 53** "When Work and Its Labours Feel Good" by Lianne Carley. Courtesy of *TG* Magazine; **p. 57** "It's Just a Matter of Time" by Helen Wilkinson. This article originally appeared in *The Idler* (January 1995), London, England. Reprinted by permission; **p. 60** "Employability Skills Profile". "Employability Skills Profile: What Are Employers Looking For" Brochure 1992 E/F (Ottawa: The Conference Board of Canada, 1992); **p. 62** "Parachute" by Lenrie Peters. From *Selected Poetry* by Lenrie Peters, Heinemann Educational Books, 1981. Reprinted by permission of the author; **p. 64** "Eight Days a Week" by Linda Lewis. Reprinted by permission of the author; **p. 71** "When the Job Sneaks Into Your Dreams" by Caleb Solomon. Reprinted by permission of *The Wall Street Journal*. © 1993 Dow Jones & Company, Inc. All Rights Reserved Worldwide; **p. 74** "When You Reach 65, Don't Be Surprised...." by John Kettle. Reprinted by permission of the author; **p. 76** "Choosing Our Future" by Jeremy Rifkin. Adapted from *The End of 'Work': The Decline of the Global Labor Force and the Dawn of the Post Market Era* (Jeremy P. Tarcher/Putnam). Reprinted by permission of Jeremy Rifkin; **p. 78** "Song of the Accountant" by Doug Elves. First appeared in *Other Voices*, Vol. 5, No. 1, Spring 1992. Reprinted by permission of Doug Elves; **p. 80** "The Carpenter" by Patrick Lane.

From *Selected Poems* by Patrick Lane, Oxford University Press, 1987. Reprinted by permission of the author; **p. 82** "The Yeoman of the Garbage" by Anthony Jenkins. Reprinted by permission of *The Globe and Mail;* **p. 88** "The Baker" by Lorna Crozier. From *Inventing the Hawk* by Lorna Crozier. Used by permission of the Canadian Publishers, McClelland & Stewart, Toronto; **p. 90** "Out of Sight of Land" by Joan Skogan. From *Voyages: At Sea With Strangers* by Joan Skogan. Copyright © 1992 by Joan Skogan. Published by HarperCollins Publishers Ltd.; **p. 97** "Pilot" by William Klebeck. "Pilot" has been previously published in *Grain*, Vol. 20, No. 1 (Spring, 1992) and in the anthology *Stag Line: Stories by Men*, Coteau Books, Spring, 1995. Reprinted by permission of the author; **p. 105** "Bound Upon a Wheel of Fire" by Sallie Tisdale. First published by *Harper's* in January, 1990. Copyright © 1990 Sallie Tisdale. Reprinted by permission of the author; **p. 113** "That Ain't Working" by Bill Sass. Reprinted by permission of *The Edmonton Journal;* **p. 120** "The Painter" by Robert D. Hoeft. Reprinted by permission of the author; **p. 121** "Debbie Tewa: Building a Future With Her Community" by Winona LaDuke. Reprinted with permission from *Indigenous Woman*, Vol. 1, No. IV. Available from IWN, P. O. Box 174, Lake Elmo, MN 55042 USA; **p. 125** "Sweetheart" by Molly Martin. Originally published in *Tradeswoman*, Winter 1988 issue. Reprinted by permission of the author; **p. 132** "Think Like a Weightlifter, Think Like a Woman" by Kate Braid. Reprinted with permission from *More Than Our Jobs: An Anthology*, edited by Glen Downie and Pam Tranfield (Arsenal Pulp Press, 1991); **p. 134** "Putting Value on Housework" by Katrin Nagelschmitz. Reprinted by permission of the author; **p. 137** "None of This is Fair" by Richard Rodriguez. Copyright © 1977 by Barbara Berg. Reprinted by permission of Georges Borchardt, Inc. for the author; **p. 142** "Jorge the Church Janitor Finally Quits" by Martín Espada. From *Rebellion Is the Circle Of a Lover's Hands* by Martín Espada (Curbstone Press, 1990). Reprinted by permission of the publisher; **p. 144** "Room For All" by Christine Micklewright. Reprinted with permission from *More Than Our Jobs: An Anthology*, edited by Glen Downie and Pam Tranfield (Arsenal Pulp Press, 1991); **p. 149** "Greetings from the Electronic Plantation" by Roger Swardson. From *City Pages*, October 21, 1992 issue. Reprinted by permission; **p. 157** "The Mind-Style of the Entrepreneur" by Michael Warshaw. First appeared in *Success*, April 1993. Written by Michael Warshaw. Reprinted with permission of *Success* Magazine. Copyright © 1993 by Success Partners; **p. 164** "Murder, Inc." by Robert Sherrill. Reprinted by permission of the author; **p. 176** "Portrait of a Machine" by Louis Untermeyer. From *Long Feud* by Louis Untermeyer published by Harcourt Brace Jovanovich, Inc. Reprinted by permission of Laurence S. Untermeyer; **p. 177** "Chicken and Fingers" by Mary Maxwell. Mary Maxwell is a writer living in Western Canada. She writes poetry and short stories as well as social justice journalism. She hopes to contribute to the effort of giving working-class women a voice so that they will no longer be "mute figures in our cultural landscape."; **p. 184** "Time and Motion Study" by Adrian Mitchell. Taken from *For Beauty Douglas* by Adrian Mitchell published by Allison & Busby. Reprinted by permission of the Peters Fraser & Dunlop Group Ltd.; **p. 185** "Action Will be Taken" by Heinrich Böll, translated by Leila Vennewitz. Reprinted by permission of Leila Vennewitz. Reprinted by arrangement with Verlag Kiepenheuer & Witsch, c/o Joan Daves Agency as agent for the proprietor. Copyright 1966 by Heinrich Böll; **p. 190** "Ogun" by Edward Kamau Brathwaite. Reprinted from *The Arrivants* by Edward Kamau Brathwaite (1973) by permission of Oxford University Press; **p. 193** "Labours and Loves" by Val Ross. Reprinted by permission of *The Globe and Mail;* **p. 196** From *Writing Down the Bones*, by Natalie

Goldberg © 1986; Reprinted by arrangement with Shambhala Publications, Inc., 300 Massachusetts Avenue, Boston, MA 02115; **p. 200** "The Bedquilt" by Dorothy Canfield. From *A Harvest of Stories* by Dorothy Canfield, Harcourt, Brace and Company, 1956. Reprinted by permission of Vivian Scott Hixson; **p. 209** "As Busy As We Wanna Be" by Deborah Baldwin. Originally appeared in *Utne Reader*, Jan./Feb. 1994. © 1994 Deborah Baldwin. Reprinted by permission of the author. "Spare Time" chart. Americans' Use of Time Project: Department of Sociology, University of Maryland, College Park; **p. 217** "Recreation for Special Populations: A Wheelchair Athlete's Perspective" by William Bowness. From *Leisure Enhancement* by Michael J. Leitner, copyright © 1989, The Haworth Press, Inc., Binghamton, New York. Reprinted by permission of the publisher; **p. 224** "Keeping Fit" by Nadine Gordimer. From *Jump and Other Stories* by Nadine Gordimer. Copyright © Felix Licensing BV, 1991. Reprinted by permission of Penguin Books Canada Limited; **p. 234** "In the Dove-Grey Dove-Soft Dusk" by Dennis Brutus. From *A Simple Lust* by Dennis Brutus. Reprinted by permission of Heinemann Publishers Limited; **p. 236** "A Walker's Manual" by Bette Pesetsky. From *Stories Up To a Point* by Bette Pesetsky. Copyright © 1978, 1979, 1980, 1981, 1982 by Bette Pesetsky. Reprinted by permission of Alfred A. Knopf, Inc.; **p. 241** "The Trout Pond" by Milton Acorn. From *Dig Up My Heart* by Milton Acorn. Used by permission of the Canadian Publishers, McClelland & Stewart, Toronto; **p. 242** "After Apple-Picking" by Robert Frost. From *The Poetry of Robert Frost* edited by Edward Connery Lathem. Copyright © 1958 by Robert Frost. Copyright © 1967 by Leslie Frost Ballantine. Copyright 1930, 1939, © 1969 by Henry Holt and Co., Inc. Reprinted by permission of Henry Holt and Co., Inc.; **p. 244** "Tired" by Shel Silverstein. From *A Light in the Attic* by Shel Silverstein. Copyright © 1981 by Evil Eye Music, Inc. Selection reprinted by permission of HarperCollins Publishers; **p. 245** "To Be of Use" by Marge Piercy. From *Circles on the Water* by Marge Piercy. Copyright © 1982 Marge Piercy. Reprinted by permission of Alfred A. Knopf. Inc.

PHOTOGRAPHS

p. 3 & p. 12 Robert Garrard; **p. 15** Photo courtesy David Weale Collection; **p. 21** CALVIN AND HOBBES © Watterson. Reprinted with permission. (Dist. by UNIVERSAL PRESS SYNDICATE). All rights reserved; **p. 48** Dick Hemingway; **p. 56** Joel Johnson/Native Indian/Inuit Photographers' Association; **p. 87** City of Toronto, Department of Public Works and the Environment; **p. 96** National Film Board of Canada/neg. no. 65-6548; **p. 119 & p. 131** Dick Hemingway; **p. 148** William James Collection (#136-A) City of Toronto Archives; **p. 192** Robert Garrard; **p. 210** Dick Hemingway; **p. 223** Canada Wide/Hugh Wesley; **p. 235** Robert Garrard.